The Road
to
Buckskin Joe

The Road to Buckskin Joe
Copyright © 2014 by Tom Knebel
All rights reserved. Printed in United States of America
First Edition

For information, address Tom Knebel, PO Box 88, Fort Collins, Colorado 80521;
E-mail: RoadToBuckskinJoe@gmail.com

Front cover design by Karen Cannon
Back cover design by Rebecca Hill

Fiction, history, Colorado Territory, gold rush

ISBN-13: 978-0-692-22999-6 (trade paperbacck)

Published by Tom Knebel, Fort Collins, Colorado

The Road
to
Buckskin Joe

Written and illustrated by

Tom Knebel

Contents

"Well done, Miss Silverheels,
wherever you are.
Well done."

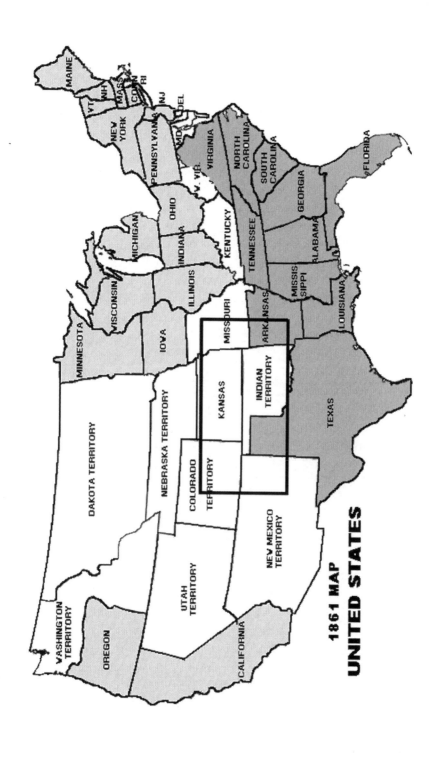

1861 MAP
UNITED STATES

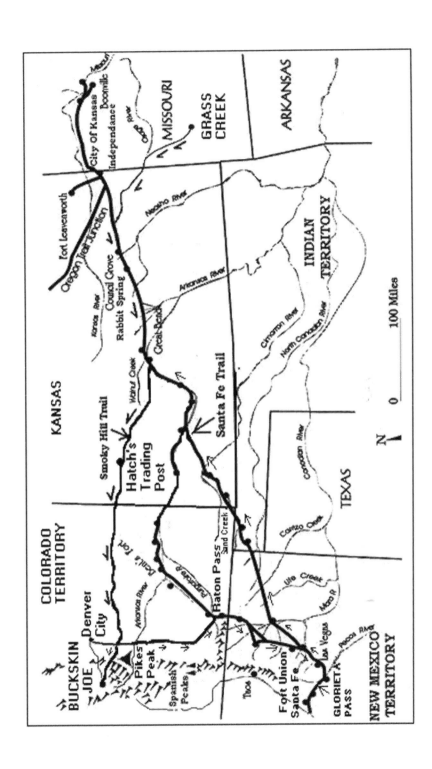

There are two rocking chairs on my porch. They both face in a direction which allows us to watch the laying of steel tracks in the median in front of my College Avenue home. I am now sitting in one of these chairs writing on a beautiful May morning in the year of our Lord 1912. My daughter Christina has just helped me into this chair, as she has each morning this spring. The other chair remains empty; not even Christina will sit on it, for it was her mother's. My legs barely work, perhaps from too much walking, perhaps from my bout with smallpox, or perhaps just due to my advanced age. At sixty-seven, I do not feel old, though few men my age are still alive. While I rest in my chair, my daughter packs my belongings for the move, for I can no longer live here alone. I could call this move an adventure, I've had plenty, but if this is to be an adventure, it is not one that I look forward to. As I took care of her so many years ago, it is now time for her to care for me; that's the way the world works.

A few days ago Christina discovered some of the journals I wrote fifty years ago when I was but a lad. They had been packed in the attic of my home and had not been read for years. I read them now again with the help of my reading glass and remember with fondness the many adventures I have had and how I got to this little city on the edge of the great American Plains: Fort Collins, Colorado.

1

Though she has heard me tell of my escapades for over thirty years, Christina wishes that I put this diary, along with a few sketches I made, into a book form so that my grandchildren, all my future descendants, and anyone interested may learn how I came to Colorado during a most turbulent time in our country.

It has been fifty years since I got the fever to move and what a half century this has been. I came here on foot in 1861, as did thousands of others, to a raw and untamed portion of the Kansas Territory. Now this new state we call Colorado has a modern railway system, fine schools and businesses, and nearly a half million people. Someday soon I will be able to board an electric street car on those tracks now being laid and ride on those rails to other parts of the city and perhaps to other nearby towns. I now have clean water pumped to the inside of my house through an underground piping system, and a telephone in the parlor. I never could have dreamed of such conveniences all those years ago.

I shall, with the help of my journal, write of my adventures to share with my grandchildren and others the thrill of being among the first to settle this great section of America.

Tom Boone
May 26, 1912

CHAPTER 1
Indians on a Sunday

Sunday, August 7, 1859

Today after church, Father went to shoot some Indians. I wanted to ride along with the Indian fighters, but they wouldn't let me go. I at least hope father gets a scalp to hang on the wall.

Old Tom

I had been writing in my journal for nearly a year, but I shall begin my story with this entry in the summer of 1859 when I was but a boy of fourteen. Until that week I was much like my father. I accepted all that I was taught and did not question his words. Church, God and hard work were all I needed to know.

3

We were farmers on the Missouri plains near the town of Grass Creek and lived in a small though cozy house.

My father, Israel Boone, who proudly proclaimed to be the great-grandson of the famed frontiersman Daniel Boone, farmed a few crops but mostly we bred, raised, and trained mules for sale to nearby farmers. I was named for my mother's maiden name, Thomas, but most people called me Tom.

My life-changing week began in church during one of those long, hot, humid, lonely summers that surely only can exist on the Missouri prairie. The church offered refuge from the grasshoppers and the hot sun, but not from the heat. Aunt May and other old women were fanning themselves fiercely while Reverend Johnson was delivering his favorite sermon: the Ten Commandments. I was more interested in meeting my friends after the service than in paying attention, but I listened to some of it:

"I am the Lord Thy God" he read. "Thou shalt have no other gods before me. Remember the Sabbath day to keep it holy. Thou shalt not kill. Thou shalt not commit adultery. Thou shalt not steal," and so on. It was when Reverend Johnson was trying to explain what bearing false witness meant that Robert Masters burst into the chapel yelling: "Indians!"

Reverend Johnson motioned him to the pulpit. Robert excitedly told us how he saw a hunting party of five Indian braves down by Raccoon Creek. The congregation seemed agitated and murmured amongst themselves.

Indians (mostly Osage) hadn't been around these parts for more than twenty years. They had ceded their lands in a treaty they didn't fully understand and were moved to reservations far to the west. On these reservations, Indians were to learn to farm, not hunt, and were never to leave Indian Territory for any reason. On this Sunday they were over a hundred miles from their "reserved land" and were hunting deer, antelope and small game.

My thoughts immediately turned to those commandments: "Thou shalt not steal"... These Osage were here to steal game that was rightly ours. "Thou shalt not kill" ... "Thou shalt not commit adultery" ... Those dirty heathen were no better than Mormons in that area of sin. "Remember the Sabbath" ... Was this not Sunday? Surely these godless savages must be punished.

Reverend Johnson ended the service abruptly and called a meeting of the men outside. It was agreed that they would ride out at once and punish this band of Indian hunters who had so boldly trespassed upon our lands. My father, because of his gallant service during the Black Hawk Wars, was chosen as the leader of the band of nine men. The newly created militia formed a circle around Reverend Johnson and the families formed an outer circle around the men.

The minister began a blessing: "Lord protect these righteous soldiers of God as they rid our land of the heathen. Bring them back safely into our folds and help us make this a land of freedom forever. Amen."

As the men rode off, my mother cried. I was moved by the quick action of the men in our church. I was proud of my father for his leadership. I was thankful that God was on our side. And I was a little fearful; for the next few hours or days, I would be the man of the farm.

For the next two days, with my brother Michael's help, I took over all chores related to the farm. As it was August, and well into growing season, it was not necessary to cultivate or otherwise work the crops. Feeding, watering and tending to the animals were chores that could be accomplished by mid-morning, leaving afternoons for repairs or for idle play.

Michael and I were grooming Edna the mule when Robert Masters rode up. He had been sent as a messenger of news of the hunt and to recruit more volunteers. "We got close to them within hours of leaving the church," he reported. "Hiding behind some trees at

Buffalo Head Prairie we watched as the Indians stalked a deer. Your father took aim and killed one of those filthy redskins, but the others galloped away before we could get shots off. We have pursued them for two days but can't seem to catch them."

Before he rode off I asked, "Did Father keep the scalp?"

"We chased the other four and didn't have the time for such foolishness. That Injun is crow meat now."

It was widely known that when the militia rid the area of Osage, a dozen scalps were taken to Saint Louis to be displayed. I could show now that I was a man, and retrieve a scalp to keep here locally. Mr. Groom might let me display it at his store and then I could present it as a trophy to my father for his bravery.

As Father was using our only riding horse, I would have to ride the mule, Edna. We had no saddle for Edna, so an old wool blanket would serve as my only cushion. I packed a haversack with biscuits, water, jerky, my knife, a Bible and a few odds and ends.

"I'm off to hunt rabbits for dinner," I lied to my mother. I carried Grandpa's old scatter gun in my arms and left at once feeling very brave and mature.

Buffalo Head Prairie was on the bank of Raccoon Creek and nearly an hour's ride away. To pass the time I recited Bible verses that might be applicable to my quest. My father read the Bible to us every night and required that we memorize verses including the book they came from. He quoted the Bible often as we went about our daily chores and, as I learned later, used only the parts of a verse that suited him. I would recite these verses now as I rode: "Seek, and ye shall find" – Matthew… "Whatsoever thy hand findeth to do, do so with thy might" – Ecclesiastes…."Eye for eye, tooth for tooth, hand for hand, foot for foot" – Deuteronomy…."He that honors his father shall have a long life" – Ecclesiastes.

I also recited some of his non-biblical lines: "Red as an Indian"...
"Drunk as an Indian"... "The only good Indian is a dead Indian"...
and "Lo, the poor Indian." "Lo" was the name many people gave to
any Indian, mocking a recent editorial by the noted New York Editor,
Horace Greeley in which he used the words "Lo, the Poor Indian" to
induce pity for the plight of the native plains people.

I reached Buffalo Head Prairie at about noon but found no corpse
anywhere. The sun was hot on my head as I traversed the area in ever
widening circles. An hour's search yielded no body or even clues.

Disappointed, I started for home but first needed to refill my can-
teen. I dismounted as I approached the trees near Raccoon Creek,
grabbed my canteen and scatter gun, and walked towards the cool
water. It was then that I spotted a severely wounded and barely con-
scious Indian propped against a tree. He had been shot on his left
side resulting in a very large hole under his arm. The hole had been
packed with mud from the creek.

I hid behind a tree. Things had changed. There was no body to
scalp. "Lo," the poor Indian was still alive.

Now was my chance to be a hero by killing this redskin. I not only
would get a scalp, but it would be mine to keep for ridding the world
of another savage heathen.

"Do you take Jesus Christ as your personal savior?" I yelled as
I sprang from the trees with my scatter gun pointed at his head. He
opened his eyes but said nothing.

"Then be prepared to be blown to Hell."

My fingers lacked the courage to pull the trigger, and I just stood
silently and continued to point my scatter gun at him. With great dif-
ficulty the Indian rose to his feet. It was then that I noticed that he was
my brother Michael's age, perhaps only twelve or thirteen years old.
He raised his good arm into the air and looked upward towards the
sun. "Eeewa, eeewa oh" he seemed to be chanting, though to this day

I don't know what words he was using, but he clearly seemed to be talking to his god. He abruptly stopped as if he were ready for me to complete my act and looked into my eyes. Those jet black eyes, while showing great pain, showed no fear. My fingers were still frozen.

I remember wondering if his god and my God were the same. I had been taught that there was only one god, the Christian God, and that Indians were heathens and not worth living. Was this true? If they didn't believe in God, then who was this boy talking to?

A last meal would be the Christian thing to do before I shot him. I had extra biscuits in my shirt and dropped two on the ground; as an afterthought I dropped a piece of jerky as well. He just stood there staring at me and I kept my aim on him as I stared back.

I don't remember how long we stood there with our eyes locked on each other, nor do I remember making a conscious decision to move, but I found myself slowly backing toward Edna, never taking my eye or aim away. As I prepared to mount, I also threw my blanket to the ground and placed my knife, my canteen, and a few more biscuits on top of it. I then rode Edna home.

That night in my father's absence, I read and re-read perhaps a dozen times, my favorite passages from the Book of Luke:

".... Ye have heard that it hath been said: Thou shalt love thy neighbor, and hate thine enemy.... But I say unto you, Love your enemies, bless them that curse you, do good to them that hate you, and pray for them which despitefully use you and persecute you."

While I was reading, I wondered: "Was this Indian my enemy?" I had no cause to hate him. I certainly had no good cause to take his life. Who decides whether or not a person is worthy of living? I lay awake most of the night pondering these questions. Many, including my father and those on the hunt, believe that only churchgoing Christians deserve a place in heaven and therefore are the only people who deserve a place on this earth. I now disagreed.

The next morning after chores I set off again. This time I was not after a scalp; I would kill no one. I would sneak food, medicine and bits of cloth for bandages to the Indian boy in the hope that he could survive the wounds that my father had inflicted on him. If my father ever found out what I was doing, he would certainly have yet another opportunity to say his oft quoted paraphrase from Proverbs: "Spare the rod and spoil the child."

When I arrived at the creek, I found a small circle of rocks where I had laid my blanket, knife, and canteen. Inside the circle was a six-inch-long hand crafted knife made from flint attached to a deer's horn carved to look like the head of an eagle. With it was a finely stitched deer hide sheath with the fur to the inside and multicolored beads decorating the outside.

My Indian was gone.

My father and the other men returned after four days, disappointed that they were unable to ever catch the hunting party but proud that they had "left one for the buzzards to finish." I said nothing. I hid my new flint knife. I then told my father that Edna had bucked me off of her back and that my belongings must be scattered on the ground miles from home, and he believed me.

I never heard what became of my Indian. Perhaps he died of his wounds. Perhaps another militia found him and taught him yet another lesson. Or perhaps, as I like to think, he safely walked the hundred plus miles to his family on the reservation.

Years later, I discovered the poem, "Essay on Man," by Alexander Pope which had inspired some of Horace Greeley's famous and oft ridiculed editorial. It includes these lines:

> Lo! the poor Indian, whose untutor'd mind
> Sees God in clouds, or hears him in the wind...
> Yet simple Nature to his hope has giv'n
> Behind the cloud-topped hill, an humbler heaven.

CHAPTER 2
Gold Fever

Old Tom

As I sit here reading this fifty-year-old journal, I remember with fondness my excitement over a recent discovery of gold in the Rocky Mountains. I wrote much in my diary in the next few months, and a reader will need little explanation from me except for perhaps a little historical background.

The year was 1860, and I was now a fifteen-year-old boy still living on a farm in Missouri with my parents and my brother Michael.

The country was in turmoil that year over the institution of slavery. Missouri officially was a slave state as were about half of the states in the Union, but most slaves in that state were concentrated near the farming areas along the Mississippi and Missouri Rivers, well away from my home near Grass Creek.

Friday, May 4, 1860

It is dark out and we just got in from the field with barely enough light to tend to the animals. This morning I was feeding and watering the livestock before dawn as I will again in just a few hours. Am I a slave? Tonight at dinner I asked Father for some money to buy a book. I do not even know which book I want to buy, how much one costs, or even where to find one for sale, but Father says he will not spare even a penny for such foolishness.

"If you wish to read,' he said, "read the Bible."

"I have read the Bible twice. I wish to learn more," I answered.

"We have no money to waste," he answered, and the conversation was over.

I am nearly sixteen years old and it is time to plan my future. I wish for it to hold an abundance of books, adventure, and excitement. Farming holds no rewards for me, and I do not see myself staying here much longer. Sometimes I hear the phrase "Go West Young Man."

I wonder…

Sunday, May 6, 1860

Today I went hunting with Jake. Father allowed me to hunt on the Sabbath so long as I went to church first. He even allowed me to take Grandfather's old scatter gun, while Jake hunted with his fine new Hawken rifle from St. Louis. We agreed before we left to equally divide whatever game we shot. The Hawken, while as fine a gun as there is, was of no use today for all we came upon were grouse. I shot six, gave Jake three, and Mother cooked the other three for dinner tonight with potatoes and onions. They were delicious!

Jake has a hankering for adventure that even exceeds mine. He has been talking frequently about the Pike's Peak gold rush, wants to go there, and wishes for me to go with him. Pike's Peak is most certainly to the west. Melvin Good and Douglas Moyer left from town about two weeks ago. I have every desire to become wealthy, and I think that an adventure to the western mountains is a good idea. I think that bringing back a wagon full of gold is a great idea!

Old Tom

I had known Jake Lewis for years. He was one year older and a full head taller than I, but that did not prevent us from becoming good friends for we liked doing the same things. We often would go exploring together and were thrilled when we discovered something that surely no white man had ever seen before. Once we found a cave with human bones in it and imagined that the old skeleton came from an ancient civilization of women warriors, though we didn't know what gender had died in that cave.

We hunted together, we fished together, and we wagered on any competition we could invent. If we were at the creek catching frogs, we held frog races; on the prairie we held snake races, and so on. We seldom held foot races for Jake would surely always win while games of intellect were out of the question as I would be the dominant one.

Jake's family owned the hotel in Grass Creek. His life was less toilsome than mine as he did not have to work from sunup to sundown following a mule. He was not lazy. He labored avidly when he had to; he just did not have to work very often except for helping around the hotel.

At the time of this diary Missouri was a slave state, but there were no slaves within miles of Grass Creek for it had been settled by farmers from the nearby states of Ohio, Illinois and Indiana. Most people there were very much against the institution of slavery. I would some-times see Negro slaves as they traveled through the area doing busi-ness with their masters, though I had no interaction with them. The only colored people in town were two freed slaves from Kentucky, who by law had to leave that state within six months of emancipation.

Auntie Martha, about fifty years old, and her sixteen-year-old son, Mason, lived in a shack behind the hotel and worked there for Jake's parents. Missouri had a law, as well, forbidding emancipated slaves to stay in the state, but Auntie Martha and Mason had lived in that shack for three years and no one seemed to mind as long as they "stayed in their place." I did not know them well. Few people did, as it was not proper for white people to mingle with the coloreds.

Tuesday, May 8, 1860

The more I think about it, the more sense it makes to go look for gold with Jake. We could be rich by winter if we leave next week. I do not know how far the gold strike is from Grass Creek but I guess it is not too far. I now have to find the courage to tell Mother and Father that I am heading west soon.

Saturday, May 12, 1860

Tonight the courage came, but it did not go well. I am still angry. They say that I am too young and they need me on the farm right now. Why do I have to wait until after the harvest? If I leave in Octo-ber, I won't reach the mountains until winter. How can I pan for gold if the streams are frozen? It will be just like the California rush ten years ago, and all the gold will soon be gone... gone even before I get there.

Many of my friends have been paid for their work on the farm. As soon as some of my friends turn sixteen, they get acreage or a horse or some means to start a life. What do I get? Another year on the farm.

They have allowed that I may leave next spring after my sixteenth birthday, but certainly with no gift of money or livestock as they cannot afford it. I should be happy, but I am not. Tomorrow we begin planting corn.

Monday, May 28, 1860

Planting is over and cultivating won't start for another week but Father keeps me busy mending fences and making repairs. My back hurts, my feet hurt, and my hands are calloused. I hate farming. That place that some now call Colorado is the answer to this misery! If I can only get my wish to leave this place, I may be two feet deep in gold in two months. I hear that you can just pick nuggets out of the stream as they glisten in the sun. I want to be wealthy and never follow a mule again. Instead of being wealthy in two months I will still be poor and slaving away two feet deep in weeds and dirt.

I think Mother and Father are getting used to the idea of me leaving but are getting weary of me talking about it all the time. I just cannot stop thinking about the fortune I will soon discover. Mother cries a lot at the thought, but it is not as if I am dying. I'm just leaving until I'm rich enough to come back to Grass Creek and build a dry goods store.

Monday, June 4, 1860

I have been asking Father for a week now if he would give one or two of the young mules to me for my travel and for a solid week he has refused. Tonight I offered him a hundred dollars for one of the unbroken three year olds if he could wait to be paid until I returned and he even refused that offer. He now accepts the idea that I am leaving in the spring and that there is little he can do about my leaving for I will be sixteen years old then. He countered the offer with, "You may have six of the donkeys if you wish."

I replied with an explanation of how silly it is to try to ride a donkey when this farm is full of young mules raring to travel. I upped my offer to two hundred dollars and he just glared at me.

After saying, "You have not even considered the supplies you may need, or how you would carry them hundreds of miles across nothing but desert," he demanded that the conversation end immediately.

Old Tom

"The Great American Desert" was the name by which the Great Plains were known back then. It was a vast short grass prairie inhabited by millions of buffalo and a few thousand Indians. Other than a handful of trails across it, there was little of what we like to think of today as "civilization."

…As I lay here writing, I think about my father's biting words for I have not even thought about supplies or money. I wonder what I need?

Tuesday, June 5, 1860

Though I am still angry, perhaps Father is correct. I am not prepared for a seven hundred mile sojourn without supplies. I need to collect food and gear for my travels and a means to carry them. I also need money, not to mention a horse.

Though he remains firm in his denial of a horse or mule, he has allowed those three jack asses and three jennies, but little else in the way of provisions. What worthless creatures donkeys are! The only good a jackass does is to breed mules and a jenny serves only to breed more jacks. You cannot ride a donkey, eat a donkey or milk a donkey. I know of no one who considers a donkey worthy of even a name. A good horse or mule can carry more than half a dozen asses can, and we now have six mules ready to be sold. For all my hard work on this farm I feel I deserve perhaps one or two of these fine animals…and a wagon… as I deserve to ride, not walk to the gold fields.

Donkeys! Good Word!

Saturday, June 9, 1860

I am earning money! The road into Grass Creek from Thomasville is being improved and the county is paying farmers forty cents a wagon load to haul gravel from the pit to be spread over the heavily-traveled dirt trail. Father won't allow me to use our wagon but lets me use a team of mules to help out. Our mules are the finest in the county and strong. Many teams are not strong enough to pull the wagons of gravel out of the pit so I charge farmers a half dime to pull their heavy loads up the steep sloping track. I make forty to sixty cents on a good evening. I may have twenty dollars by summer's end. I may for the first time in my life walk into Mr. Groom's store and buy a penny's worth of peppermint candy without having to beg for coins out of Mother's egg money. I'll save most of my earnings to buy necessary supplies when the time comes.

Sunday, June 10, 1860

Today is Sunday, and Jake and I went hunting after church again. I had Edna to ride and Jake was on Muffin, his chestnut mare. With him was the colored boy, Mason, on Jake's father's horse. I was nervous. What would people say if they saw me with a former slave as if he were an equal?

Jake laughed at my uneasiness. "Why do you care what people think?"

I had no answer. All day long my mind was filled with that question.

Mason is the same age as Jake and me and seems little different from us other than the color of his skin, the way he talks, and his ever present limp as he walks around with a crutch under his arm. He did not carry a gun of any kind, as Negroes are not permitted weapons in Missouri. I have not even witnessed a colored person riding a horse before as the Negroes I see are walking beside a wagon load of goods or are driving a coach for their masters. I wonder if any laws were broken allowing Mason to ride a horse? I wonder if I could get into trouble for being with a colored person on a horse?

We hunted for about two hours, found nothing, and spent the rest of the day fishing in Buffalo Creek about a mile from town. As we sat there with our lines lazily drifting in the slow moving water, the three of us talked, laughed, discussed religion and politics and slavery and girls, and paid little heed to our fishing.

Mason knew or cared very little about politics other than how it affects slavery. He did not even know that James Buchanan is our President. He cannot read or write and felt uncomfortable talking about girls, as all girls in town are white and unavailable to him for any kind of contact. He did have plenty to say about slavery and told us what it was like to be a slave, working all day long in the fields with no pay. His master would whip him if he felt Mason was not working hard enough. Mason has two brothers and two sisters somewhere in Kentucky, but he has not seen them since they were sold to other slave holders when they turned twelve. He would have been sold as well, had he owned two good legs, but few want a Negro who cannot work well in the fields. As I write this, I see that Mason may be quite different from me after all.

I caught a catfish, one large enough to supply dinner for the family tonight, and Mother fried it in corn meal. When I told her that Mason went with us, her only reaction was to say, "Oh my!" I did not tell Father. I suspect that mother did not tell him either.

As the town of Grass Creek has but seventy or so people in it, I know most everyone quite well. I know something personal about each person. For the past three years, since his arrival, I have only watched as Mason limped about town performing errands for the hotel. I had not spoken to him once, for he did not attend school, church, or any social activity. Negroes are allowed in Mr. Groom's store, but neither he nor his mother ever speaks to customers.

Until today I did not know why Mason limps so badly and needs that crutch under his arm to walk. I did not know how he and his mother became free, and I did not know why they picked Grass Creek to be their home. Until today I did not care.

I now know that Mason fell out of a tree when he was 10 and did not have proper doctoring to mend his broken leg. He got whipped by his master for climbing that tree. I know now that Mason and his mother were the only two slaves on a small farm in Kentucky for a childless couple. When the farmer died, the wife did not wish to continue to be a slave holder as she did not believe in the institution of slavery. A freed slave in Kentucky must leave the state immediately, and these two people had nowhere to go. Freed slaves also have a good chance of being captured, their papers destroyed, and being resold back into slavery. She wrote to her sister in Missouri and found employment for the two as servants in a hotel. That sister is Jake's mother. Grass Creek is a safe place for them to live as this is an area of little slavery. Though they are free to leave, they chose to stay here and work at the hotel for little money, even though the prospect of being captured and sold is very real. Few may want to pay much for Mason or his mother, as he can barely walk and his mother is old, but the threat of capture is very possible nevertheless.

As I sit here writing tonight, I continue to ponder Jake's question. "Why do you care what people think?" I like Mason. Jake jokingly calls him "Free Mason" and talks to him as if he were an old friend. Perhaps they are old friends, for Mason has lived at the hotel for three years. Why did I not know that Jake considers Mason to be his friend? What would happen to me if people saw me being friendly towards Mason? ...and again, why do I care what people think? It is again time for me to do research in the Bible for answers.

Thursday, June 14, 1860

If the Bible has all the answers, then why are the questions so well hidden? I find nothing that gives any directions for "Why should I care what people think if I associate with Mason?" For that matter "Why should I care what people think about anything I do?" I asked Father and he tells me to just obey God's laws and stay away from the coloreds. Reverend Johnson agrees.

Sunday, June 17, 1860

Today after church Jake let me borrow his book, "Gold Discoveries on the South Platte River: a Guide of the Route" by Smith & Oaks. It is a guide book on the routes to the gold fields. He bought it in St. Louis when he went with his father for hotel supplies last week. He let me take notes of the supplies needed: large cloth bags (not crates) of corn meal, flour, dried apples, and salt pork (at least a sixty day supply), plus three pairs of shoes, six flannel shirts, an army type coat and boots, a musket, plenty of matches and so on and so on. The book also contained advertisements for trading posts along the trail where you could purchase such items. Jake has plenty of money and plans to travel light and outfit himself along the way. I see now that I need more money and more supplies.

Monday, June 18, 1860

If I am to leave by early spring, I shall exit this land in sad condition. I have six worthless donkeys and little else. It will take me 'til spring to acquire provisions. I will need six pack saddles, rope, a shovel, food for two months, money, blankets, canvas, and who knows what else? I have grandfather's old scatter gun, but I need powder and pellets. April is only eight months away, and I need to start working for others to earn some of these things. Father works me until I am weary, but I have a few leisure hours after dinner on those few days I am not working at the gravel pit. Widder Hultgren has alfalfa to cut. I shall ask her tomorrow.

Tuesday, July 10, 1860

I have a canvas now and half a dollar. Widder Hultgren traded me a fine old canvas for cutting her acre of alfalfa. It was hard work and took me a week of evenings to cut it, and the heat was torturous. The half dollar piece came as a reward for the effort I made. For the August cutting she will give me an ox hide her husband tanned before he passed on. I shall work hard again and hope for yet another silver piece.

Wednesday, August 1, 1860

When time allows, I have been working for Mrs. Hultgren. She invites me into her home when I am finished with whatever chore she has given me to do. As I sit with her at her table drinking a fresh glass of milk and eating cookies, she tells me stories of the early days in Missouri. She moved here with her husband, Gustov, over thirty years ago, a few years after Missouri became a state, and helped him to develop their eighty acre farm. She even helped him to build the sturdy little cottage that she now lives in. As I get to know her, I regret that I referred to her as Widder Hultgren. She is aware of the name, but prefers to be called Ethel or Mrs. Hultgren. I shall call her the latter as she is almost sixty years old and deserving of my respect. As she is getting on in years, she is soon to move to St. Louis to live with her daughter, Amanda and her husband, Ben. She will move in November by buggy and must consolidate her possessions, and I shall help her clean her property for a quick sale. For this help she is giving me some of her late husband's possessions: scraps of leather and buckles from which to make straps for my pack saddles, an axe, plenty of gunpowder and shot for my scatter gun, plus items from her barn that I would not have thought of: a saw, lamp oil, a hammer, nails, a tin pail and a piece of heavy tin which I can use to hammer out a gold pan.

She also gave me a small bent iron contraption that she called an Ozark jaw harp. She said that many travelers carry musical instruments with them such as a fiddle or a fife, but Mr. Hultgren did not own or know how to play one. A blacksmith hammered this small instrument out of iron so that he would have music on his travels. I, too, do not own or know how to play music, but when I held this contraption to my teeth, I could blow air while I vibrated a sliver of wood attached to the bent iron. Crude as it sounded, I now had a musical instrument that I could keep in my pocket.

Friday, August 3, 1860

Today I raked Mrs. Hultgren's yard as she was inside packing books into wooden crates. She summoned me inside her house, and I thought that I was about to get a hot cup of coffee, but what she had was much better. "Here, you need this more than I do" and she gave me the one possession of her late husband that I shall treasure forever … his Mexican war journal. Few men from these parts were literate sixteen years ago, and Gustov Hultgren was one of those few. At the age of forty he joined a Missouri battalion in William Kearney's "Army of the West" and marched from here to Santa Fe and then on to California in 1846 to free the West from Mexican control. His ability to read and write made him a favorite of Colonel Kearney and his duty was to scribe an official log for the colonel. He also kept a log for himself of which I am now in possession. It includes valuable maps of the Santa Fe Trail, locations of water holes, and details of the terrain. I protested that her daughter would want this book more than I, but Mrs. Hultgren just shook her head and said "Gus would have liked you. Maybe this journal will keep you safe on your journey."

Mrs. Hultgren also loaned me a book on how to draw but told me that I must return it before she leaves as she wishes it for her grandchildren.

Friday, August 10, 1860

I am trying to learn how to draw so that I might record my journey as Gustov Hultgren did. Maps are easy, houses are not too difficult, but sketches of animals and people are almost impossible. The book says that parallel lines meet at the horizon, and showed railroad tracks as an example. I have never seen railroad tracks or even a straight road to prove this to my satisfaction but I draw houses that way and they look good. I wonder where parallel lines are on people, or any lines for that matter. I drew a pretty good picture of my jaw harp and I am now trying to draw a sketch of what I want my pack saddles to look like. I try to draw pigs, horses and even donkeys, but they are not very good. Father says that I cannot waste paper on foolishness, so I do most of my practice drawing on a piece of slate with a white rock that I found near Raccoon Creek. If I wish to make a log of my journey I will have to save money to buy ink and a lot of paper. If I can afford it I will also buy a pen with a metal point so that I do not have to take a lot of goose feathers.

Sunday, August 19, 1860

At church today Jake and I compared resources. He has a hundred dollars compared to my eight. He has a mule, Hay Burner, and a horse, Muffin, and good saddles for each, while I have six lousy donkeys without saddles or even names for that matter. He has no equipment but I have the canvas and much of the gear that once belonged to Gustov Hultgren. Jake is concerned about the slow pace I will take by walking with six donkeys but still wishes to travel with me in the spring. I am glad to have a traveling companion and am happy it will be Jake. Unlike so many my age who only want to stay on the farm, Jake has the same urge for adventure that I have.

Today mother confided to me that I take after the more itinerant Thomas side of the family and that she understands my desire to seek out new places and adventures. She reminded me that my great-great grandfather Daniel Boone was an explorer who would move whenever he could see the smoke from a neighbor's fire, but since his departure from this earth the Boones in this area have been stay-at-home farmers and not of the pioneering sort.

Old Tom

My mother, Elizabeth, was the daughter of a circuit preacher. When she was young, she traveled with my grandfather to whichever town on the frontier the Methodist church desired a new mission, no matter how isolated. She lived in Iowa, Minnesota, and parts of Illinois before they were civilized. She loved traveling to remote places and I got my sense of adventure from her. Grandfather was a master of the collection plate and for six months each year was able to send her to a fine finishing school in Baltimore where she learned not only good social graces but gained an insatiable reading appetite. She met my then eighteen-year-old father near the frontier town of Grass Creek in 1840, fell in love, and married him at age sixteen. Gone forever were her thrilling days of travel and learning. They built their farm on a tract of land two miles from town and lived there for the rest of their lives. At the time of this journal, my mother lived a fairly solitary life. The only people she talked to on a regular basis were my father, my twelve year old brother, Michael, and me. She treasured Sundays where she could socialize with other women at church. Though I was schooled for six years at a one room school near here, my education and quest for learning came from her. I used her vocabulary and not the language of my fellow Grass Creek friends. Mother owned a few books including a Bible, and I read them all many times.

My father's passion was farming. He started his mule farm from a humble land grant and did most of the work himself. Forty acres were broken from the tall grass of the Missouri prairie for farming crops, and the other one hundred and twenty acres was devoted to pasture land. At the time of this journal I was nearly sixteen years old and soon would be capable of acquiring, with his help, more acres to expand his dream of a very large mule breeding operation. I now understand his anger and disappointment at my eagerness to leave the farm. But I had learned much from my mother, and I knew that there was more to this world than Missouri and farming. What I needed at that age was adventure, which might explain the following excerpts:

Saturday, August 25, 1860

Tonight a conversation went very badly. I am so bothered by it that I shall write it down as best as I can remember so that I may understand why it went so wrong:

"Pass the beans, please," I requested shortly after Father said the supper blessing.

"Tom, why don't you marry Becky Thompson, start that farm we've been talking about, and forget this gold nonsense," was his reply.

"Pike's Peak or bust and pass the beans," I responded, and Michael, sitting next to me, broke out laughing.

"May God forgive your disrespectful mouths!" Mother snapped. "No more sass or talk of Pike's Peak or gold again."

Father's face reddened as he continued, "I hear Widder Hultgren is putting her farm up for sale. If you must leave home, why don't we arrange to buy it? I know she likes you, and she might allow you to purchase it with regular payments."

I said nothing, for life surely has finer rewards than farming or mule breeding or Becky Thompson for that matter.

My silence made Father red with anger. "If you don't get yourself killed you will probably see the elephant and come home penniless. Do not expect a hearty welcome."

Old Tom

"Seeing the elephant" was a popular expression when talking about the gold rush. About 1840 a man found giant mastodon bones buried near a riverbank and assembled them in St Louis to create a

24

museum. This elephant was truly enormous and frightening to those who had never seen such a thing. "Seeing the elephant" came to symbolize the westward expansion as many traveling through St Louis on their way West stopped to see the bones. That man stuck two red glass balls in the Mammoth's eye sockets to make it seem fiercer and claimed that giant elephants might still roam the West. The elephant came to symbolize the awe and fear travelers had for this yet untamed land. If you saw the elephant rising out of the darkness with those furious red eyes, he was telling you that it was time to turn around and go home. Many wagons which once headed west with banners proudly exclaiming "Pike's Peak or bust," headed back east with humble signs saying "seen the Elephant."

At that time, I had determined that I would never use the phrase "seen the elephant" as an expression of defeat. A few days later I wrote in my diary;

Sunday, August 26, 1860

Father thinks I shall "see the elephant" and run home in shame. He is wrong! I shall not only seek out that "elephant" that is the West. I will ride him!

Saturday, September 1, 1860

Today Becky Thompson stopped by the farm. I don't get many visitors, especially female ones, so this was an unusual happening…

Old Tom

I had known Becky all my life for she lived just a half mile away on a neighboring farm. A year younger than I, she was the closest of any neighbors to being my age. Becky had always been a tomboy so I considered her to be a playmate and nothing more. Lately when we met, however, we would talk instead of playing games, and on this September morning she seemed different… more grown up…prettier.

25

...She carried a basket of what I hoped was fresh fruit or a warm pie but I soon found that it was a basket of warm puppies, four puppies in all and all dressed in various shades of brown. "You will need a friend on your journey, one who will warn you of danger and listen to your endless talking" she said. I agreed, and not worried about my parent's opinion, I chose the restless one. She was the color of coffee with just a touch of cream. "Consider this fine young lady to be an early Christmas Present," Becky said as she put the puppy gently into my arms. "Then I shall name her Holly and think of you when the Christmas winds blow gold dust under my door," I replied. Becky stayed about twenty minutes and left when I was summoned back to my chores.

As she walked down the lane towards her home, I noticed that she is getting a nice womanly figure, and I began to think that those fun days of climbing trees and exploring caves with her may be over for she no longer looks like that bratty child next door. Then I realized that I am no longer interested in climbing trees and exploring caves, myself, for I have a thousand mile adventure ahead of me and something waiting for me when I get there! Gold!

Friday, September 21, 1860

It has been raining a lot lately, and I have been finding time to make pack saddles. Father has a saddle in the barn for when he takes Edna out on a hunt, and I have been making miniature versions of it. I cut oak boards and fashion them with a draw knife to match the curve of a donkey's back. Then with hardware that Mrs. Hultgren gave me from her husband's supply, I bolt these boards together. I then make halters and straps out of that old ox hide and buckles.

Tonight I finished my sixth saddle and soon I will start training my donkeys to carry these packs.

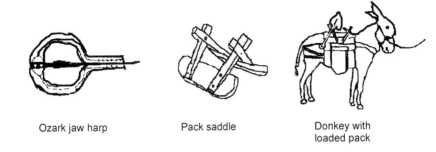

Ozark jaw harp   Pack saddle   Donkey with
loaded pack

Tuesday, October 2, 1860

It rained again yesterday so today was too wet for the harvest. Though I still wish for a horse or mule I have come to accept that I shall walk to the gold fields pulling six lowly donkeys. At noon I separated out these useless animals and put them in the fenced acre that we normally use for training mules. I put halters on each of them, and after some quarrelling, we finally agreed on who was in charge…me.

I was able to connect all six together by rope into a train. Two of my donkeys were cooperative and I found that putting them at the head of the train worked best. Though some may think that the naming of a donkey is as odd as the naming of a chicken, I gave each of these two animals a name. The jack shall be called Adam, and the jenny will be Eve. Two of the jacks are rather unruly. I put those two at the rear of the train and named them Cain and Abel because I wanted to slay them both. The two jennies in the middle don't have names yet, so I just call them Number 3 and Number 4 for their places in the train. After a bit of a struggle, I placed all of my newly-made pack saddles on six blanketed backs. We walked around the fenced acre for nearly an hour before I was pleased with their cooperation. Every few minutes I added bags of rocks to their loads until they were each carrying one hundred pounds, more or less. Holly followed for the entire hour and barked playfully at their heels. She seems to know how to keep them under control and I think that Holly may prove to be a valuable companion on my journey.

Thursday, October 4, 1860

Holly usually sleeps on the porch and greets me each morning to walk with me to the spring. Today she was not there to welcome me and I walked down the lane with my two water buckets by myself. As I passed by the fenced acre I spotted my Holly. She was with the six donkeys and playing as if the donkeys were fellow dogs. The surprising thing was that they seemed to not mind her and actually enjoyed her companionship. It took a whistle from me to get her attention and to follow me to the spring. She then followed me throughout the day as I did my chores and helped with the harvest but stayed out of the way of the mules and wagons. What a fine dog she is becoming; I am glad she will be walking with me to the gold fields and though she is just an animal, I think that I shall never find a better friend.

Sunday, October 7, 1860

I had a new adventure today, and I cannot stop thinking about it. I walked home from church instead of riding in the wagon. My parents were talking to Becky's parents and others after the service, and it seemed as if they would chatter on forever. Jake was absent from church today, and I was just standing around feeling bored when Becky came up to me and suggested that we walk home together.

"Why would I walk when I can ride in a wagon with my family?" I asked.

"Because we will get home quicker," she said. "Are your legs broken?"

I feared that Michael and his friends would tease me for walking with a girl, but because it was such a nice day for October, I agreed. Our parents seemed surprised that we would rather walk than ride but consented. Though I have walked that road home a hundred times, today seemed quite different and actually enjoyable. Becky loved the autumn colors just beginning to show, pointed to things I had never paid attention to, and even found some wildflowers still blooming in the tall prairie grass beside the road and she picked some for her hair. I think that she could have put them in her hair by herself, but she asked me to do it for her. We talked the entire mile and a half distance and the walk was over far too quickly. I lingered around her farm for another half hour until Becky's mother said it was time for dinner. She invited me to stay, but I felt uneasy being there and walked home. I was late for my own dinner and had to eat cold beans, and I soon regretted not staying at Becky's house for a hot dinner of chicken and mashed potatoes.

Anymore it seems that all I ever do is work or go to church. I wonder if Becky would like to walk home again with me next Sunday.

Saturday, November 3, 1860

Today, Mrs. Hultgren left for St. Louis. She has but forty acres and her modest house remaining, as she has sold off acreage through the years to keep in money. A young couple, not much older than I am is arriving from Illinois to take over the farm. I wish them well. Perhaps farming is in their blood.

Holly and I got up before dawn and we walked to Mrs. Hultgren's place to help pack her wagon. I am not yet very talented at drawing, but I returned the book on drawing. Her daughter's husband, Ben, worked with me and we had her packed and the house cleared before noon. All possessions not needed in her new home were left for the arriving couple. I had already taken those items that were given to me by Mrs. Hultgren or earned by working.

Ben had brought a team of horses to pull the heavily loaded wagon and I tied Mrs. Hultgren's pony to the rear. I felt gloomy all morning. I know that I shall never see Ethel Hultgren again. I know that she shall never see her beloved farm again and though I know that life holds a similar end to all that are fortunate to live long enough, I still felt sorry for her. As she was being helped into her seat on the wagon by Ben, she called for me. Mrs. Hultgren reached into her bag and pulled out a book tied with a yellow ribbon. The book had no title on its cover, and inside were only blank pages.

"You remind me of my husband," she said. If he knew you, he would want you to fill his unused journal full of your youthful adventures. Make them good." She then gave me his old pen with an iron point and a half bottle of black ink. "Gus always drew pictures to go with his journal. You can draw can't you?" I nodded and tried not to tear up. Her generosity to me, while greatly appreciated, was more than I deserved.

We said our goodbyes, Ben grabbed the reins, and the wagon lurched to a slow start. I watched till they were spots in the distance and walked home feeling sad, not only for Mrs. Hultgren but for myself as I shall miss her and her stories of the early pioneering days of this area.

Sunday, November 4, 1860

Today after church a discussion got quite heated as all the men were talking politics. There is a presidential election coming up this Tuesday and everyone seems agitated about the possible outcome. My father, Becky's father, and many others favor Stephen Douglas, the Senator from Illinois. A few men like a candidate from somewhere south named John Bell and some favor a man named Breckinridge from Kentucky or some state around there. No one, but Mr. Groom, wants Abraham Lincoln to become President. Though no one in town is a slave holder, many men seemed angry that Mr. Groom would voice his approval of the candidate that has vowed to stop the progression of slavery. They think that most slave-holding states, and possibly even Missouri, might leave the Union if this man is elected. I am not the least interested in who our next president should be, but I stood there listening to the heated conversation because I really had nothing else to do.

As I stood there fidgeting, Becky walked up to me in that blue dress she wears on Sundays. She said nothing. She just looked up at me with those matching blue eyes which seemed to be asking, "Will you walk me home?"

I nodded my agreement without any words. This time we didn't ask permission, we only waved at our parents as we left. This time I did not even care that Michael and his friends followed us taunting for a while, for again we had a pleasurable half hour stroll.

Thursday, November 15, 1860

News has been arriving that Abraham Lincoln will probably be our next president. Father is troubled and says that bad things will happen. Mr. Lincoln has said that "Government cannot endure permanently half slave, half free," and father thinks he will try to do something that will ruin the South's way of life. We hear that bands of men to the North of us are harassing German farmers suspected of voting for this man. Only Mr. Groom here openly supported Mr. Lincoln and he is being very quiet about the situation. He is now worried that these men may come to town and burn his store down.

Sunday, November 18, 1860

I now walk home from church every Sunday with Becky no matter what the weather is. When I walked that same journey to and from school, it seemed like a long and boring walk, and now with the leaves mostly off the trees and the skies a dreary gray, the trek should be most tedious, but it is not.

Today we didn't talk much about flowers, leaves, or hidden wildlife; we talked about what we wanted life to hold for us.

As I frequently do, I talked nearly non stop of my plans to find gold. I told her about my supplies, my new pack saddles and complained about having to travel to the gold fields without a horse to ride. She mostly listened, but finally did say this as if it were some memorized speech for school: "I envy your sense of adventure, Tom…Going into the heart of Indian country to find your dreams is perhaps the bravest thing I have ever known someone to do, and I'm proud of you. I just want to stay here in Missouri close to my family, live in a white house with a white fence, a good husband, and four or five children."

"Children can be an adventure," I replied, "but how can you know that Missouri is where you want to live if you have never been anywhere else?"

"It's what we are supposed to do isn't it? Stay close to the family and have children, grandchildren and large family dinners?"

"I guess so," I responded, "but where are the rules written that says you, me, or anyone has to stay where we grew up? What rules keep us from seeking new frontiers?"

She shrugged her shoulders. "It's just what we are supposed to do, that's all."

As we neared her home, she asked me if I had ever seen tobacco leaves. Her father had tried planting a small plot of the crop this year and had leaves drying in an unused corn crib. He had not planted enough tobacco to sell; he had just planted enough to see if the plants could grow on his farm. Many farmers around here are experimenting with traditionally southern crops this year. If the southern states do secede as rumored, and if Missouri stays in the Union, profits on tobacco, cotton, and hemp could be huge.

I had never seen tobacco and accepted her invitation. The corn crib is a small shack sided with tree branches spaced close enough to hold cobs of corn, but far enough apart to allow air to flow through and has a tin roof to keep the rain out. We went into the crib through the door facing Becky's house. Her parents were already home from church and I do not know if they saw us enter or not. Inside the dusty crib, hanging on ropes stretched from one side to the other were hundreds of large yellow and brown leaves. Light filtered through the spaces in the branches creating eerie shadows on those leaves.

Becky grabbed a brown leaf, tore it in half and rolled the still slightly moist leaf into two balls.

"Have you ever chewed tobacco?" she asked as she handed me a ball the size of a robin's egg.

"No, I don't think I should," I answered. "It isn't right."

"Where are the rules written that says we cannot chew tobacco?" she said and popped the other ball in her mouth.

"Good Word, Becky! What would your parents think?" I asked.

"I don't care; they probably think that we are in here kissing anyway."

I had never known Becky to be so bold. Here she was slobbering, with a big wad of tobacco in her mouth, and perhaps hinting that I should kiss her.

"What are you asking me to do?" I asked.

"What do you want to do, Mr. Brave Adventure Man?"

I popped the wad in my mouth. "I need to go home." And without even checking her expression I left her standing inside that crib with a puffed out left cheek and perhaps a bewildered look on her face.

As I write this, I can only think that while she may see me as a brave adventurer I can sometimes have a yellow stripe that runs right down my back. How can I walk hundreds of miles through dangerous territory when I cannot muster the courage to kiss Becky or even know if she wants me to? Am I ready for a journey across the Great American Desert, or am I, as my father says, "too young for such foolishness."

Maybe next Sunday we can return to that old corn crib and test my courage. This time, perhaps, I can find an adventure more exciting than chewing on a foul tasting ball of weeds.

Friday, February 1, 1861

The winter shows no signs of letting up but Jake and I have decided to leave on the morning of April 1, a Monday, and only two weeks after the first day of spring. If we leave any earlier, there will be no green grass to graze the animals. If we leave later, we may not reach the gold fields until winter has reached the mountains.

By my calculations from Mr. Hultgren's journal we have over eight hundred miles to travel to reach Pike's Peak. At fifteen to twenty miles a day we should be at Pike's Peak and panning for gold by the middle of June, wealthy by July, and back home by November.

Jake frequently complains that I will slow the journey by walking and thinks that I should buy a horse. He knows that I cannot come up with the money for such a purchase but, nevertheless, he makes known his wishes on a regular basis. He is desperate for adventure and has what people around here call "gold fever." At a little over six feet in height, he is the tallest person I know; a full four inches taller than I. He has wheat colored hair, freckles still showing from child-hood, and smiles frequently. Everyone likes Jake. His impatience is the only flaw in his character that I find annoying. Jake has plenty of money and plans to travel light and outfit himself along the way. He will carry enough food and supplies for three weeks and intends to purchase goods at various trading posts along the route. I, on the other hand, have only thirty-five dollars. I may need that money for emergencies so I shall pack all those supplies plus a few extras. I only have one pair of shoes plus Mr. Hultgren's old army boots. If shoes become a problem, I do still have plenty of leather and tools and I plan to take them with me. Mrs. Hultgren gave me much of her husband's old army gear including the boots as well as rain gear, a compass, and a weathered old wool coat. Father, with a softening of heart, allowed that I take two bags of flour, one bag of corn meal, one half sack of oats for the donkeys, and one half sack of salt pork. I did not think to pick and dry apples in the fall, so I have none for the trip, but I have found plenty of walnuts lying around in the woods and I have a quarter peck of them and a few pounds of dried cherries that mother gave me from her root cellar. I also have a chunk of salt, a sack of coffee, a bag of beans, sassafras roots, and the Ozark jaw harp to make music.

Friday, March 22, 1861

Today I heard distressing news of which I must keep secret. Jake's mother, Sarah, heard rumors that officials were arriving to arrest

Mason and Auntie Martha for not leaving Missouri as is required of all freed slaves. I do not know where those two black-skinned people could go because nearly all states have laws banning freed slaves, and they have no means to travel through hostile country to those few states which do allow freed Negroes. Perhaps Jake's parents could have had papers drawn up making the two servants their legal property, perhaps they could have hidden them away someplace safe, or maybe they could have done nothing other than to wait for the authorities to arrive.

They knew that Mason and Auntie Martha could not have had a fair trial had they just waited for government men to arrive. Their only destiny would have been to again be sold into slavery, probably separately. Instead, Mrs. Lewis used her connections to have Mason and Auntie Martha "hired on" to work for an outfitted caravan heading west out of Independence for the gold fields. There are no laws against freed slaves in the new territory now called Colorado. They may live there legally but will have to watch out for those who capture black people and return them to the South for sale to slave holders. Jake and I once considered joining such an outfit, but the twenty-five dollar fee seemed too expensive and we also want to prove that we are capable of such a journey by ourselves. As Auntie Martha and Mason have no money, they will not be able to pay for the privilege of riding in a wagon. Instead they will walk beside the wagons and work for the outfitters. Auntie Martha will take along her only possessions outside of her clothing, her old tin washtub and a hot iron which the outfitting company agreed to carry for free providing that she serve as laundress and cook for the group of forty. Mason, despite his lame leg, will have to gather firewood, build fires for cooking and washing, feed the livestock, and assist his mother. Auntie Martha intends to set up a wash house in the diggings called Denver City upon her arrival.

Last Saturday Jake and his father hurried the two of them out of town under a blanket in their carriage. The two former slaves have papers showing that they indeed are free, but many men make a lot of money by capturing freed slaves, destroying those papers, and reselling these people for huge sums of money. I envy their westward departure and hope they safely arrive to find the true freedom they both wish for. Perhaps we will look them up when we arrive in Denver City.

Old Tom

I wrote little more in my journal for the next few days. I must have been very excited and busy, but no mind, I remember starting day as if it were yesterday. I awoke before dawn on the morning of April 1, saddled up the donkeys, and arranged them into a train. Eve, my favorite, would lead the train and walk slightly in front of me. I had found that she traveled more willingly if she thought that she was in charge. Her halter lead was about ten feet long and knotted on the end. I carried it in my left hand to softly use as a whip in case she chose to stop. She was to carry my personal supplies: my log book, small amounts of food and oats, my scatter gun, a knife, some rope, my extra clothing, water, and the knife the Indian boy had left for me two years earlier. (It was not necessary for my travels, but that knife was my most treasured possession.) Adam and Number 3 would each carry two bags of flour equally balanced on each side. Number Four would carry a noisy assortment of tools: a pick, a shovel, a hammer, pots, pans, nails and assorted hardware. Cain carried the corn meal, and Abel carried the canvas and my bag of miscellaneous supplies. If I were to shoot a deer or other game, he would also have to carry that. All in all, I probably had nearly five hundred pounds of supplies, enough to last four months, with Eve carrying about fifty pounds and the others each carrying a hundred pounds, more or less.

Dawn had barely broken when I entered the house. My father and Michael were already in the barn doing chores, and Mother was at the hearth cooking breakfast with two very red and moist eyes.

"I need two promises," she demanded. "First, promise to come home when the time is right."

"As I've said before, Mother, when I have the money for a freighter of goods, I will be home to start a dry goods store in Grass Creek."

She nodded, "Secondly," and then she paused to hold back tears, "don't get yourself killed."

I hugged her as I myself held back tears and assured her that I would take no unnecessary risks. Then she gave me a package wrapped in brown paper. It looked like a book, and when I opened it I recognized it as grandfather's old traveling Bible. It was smaller than our family Bible and had a leather case to keep it safe from the weather. "You need a Bible. Grandfather would want you to have this one."

Father and Michael came in from feeding the animals, and we all ate a quiet breakfast. The sun was soon up, and it was time to leave. We all walked outside and Mother was now openly crying. Father tried to reassure her. "He'll be home before winter and rich as Midas." I shook his hand goodbye and he said, "Be safe." I nodded and said nothing, for crying, like hugging, was not permissible amongst men. Though awkward, I did give Michael a one armed hug, and then I whistled for Holly and with a soft flip of my rope onto Eve's rump, we began our journey.

It was a two mile walk to Grass Creek, a distance I had walked a hundred times before and one that I usually traveled in about thirty minutes. Between my farm and the town were perhaps twelve other family farms and though most in the area knew of my venture, no one was out to greet me, except one. As I ventured past the Thompson farm, there was Becky in her blue Sunday dress carrying that familiar basket. No puppies were in it this time. To my surprise and delight, she had made me a whole basket of honey and oat cookies, fifty in all. Each was wrapped in oiled paper to keep it fresh and each was tied with a little blue ribbon.

"Don't forget me," she said.

"Thank you," I replied, "but I shall never forget you; Holly won't allow that."

Until that moment, words came easily when I talked to Becky, but a lump in my throat kept them from flowing. "I still plan to be back soon with a freighter load of goods to start that dry goods store. Remember?" She nodded. "Look me up if you need a job," I awkwardly said, though I wished to say something more poetic.

I then did something that until that moment, I had dreamed of doing but had not ventured the courage: with one hand still holding the lead rope to Eve's halter, I grabbed Becky around the waist with the other. She looked up to me with tears in her eyes, and I kissed her.

"I won't be gone long," I said and we remained hugging each other for almost a full minute. I was close to crying myself, but because being seen crying back in those days would have been a great embarrassment, I straightened myself up, gently whipped Eve in the rump with my lead rope and began walking. I walked perhaps a hundred paces before I ventured the courage to turn around. Becky was still standing there in that pretty blue dress watching me depart for an adventure that could take months. "I'll write you," I yelled, and turned again in the direction of Grass Creek. It was not until I was out of sight that I wiped the tears from my eyes. I was still eager to go on this great adventure that lay ahead of me, but I now wished that the path that lay ahead of me was an eight hundred mile walk home from church with Becky's hand in mine.

In town I found Jake saddled up and waiting. With perhaps two hundred pounds of gear on his gray mule, Hayburner, he was already astride his small chestnut mare, Muffin. Jake was in a hurry to leave, and so with no fanfare we walked west out of Grass Creek with the morning sun on our backs and hope in our eyes.

CHAPTER 3

The Trail

Tuesday, April 2, 1861 day 2

We walked about fifteen miles today and stopped to set up camp when we saw the sun was getting low. This was not enough time, for it was dark before we got to cooking supper, and the animals are still grazing as I write this though the sun set three hours ago. From now on we shall end our day much earlier, though Jake is a little disappointed that we did not travel twice the fifteen miles we made today. As I write this log by lamp light in the comfort of a shelter made with my canvas, I feel the chill of an April wind. I already miss my cozy loft in our home and worry that a month or so of traveling may prove quite toilsome. I have blisters on my feet; walking faster is not going to be easy.

Old Tom

From that day on our days would end much the same. We would stop about three hours before sunset near a watering spot. Gustov Hultgren's journal came in extremely handy, for his notes were accurate and he had recorded nearly every spring along the route. We unloaded our animals and tended to them first and then made a tent out of my canvas by placing it over two vertical poles and securely tying it to whatever tree or rock we could find. We hobbled our animals to prevent them from wandering and kept them close to us. If time allowed we would spend a short time hunting game, but a successful hunt was rare, for the trail was heavily traveled by others also wishing for fresh meat. For safety we camped in groups with as many as twenty other travelers, built one common fire and sat around it sharing news and gossip.

Always in these camps there was talk about Lincoln's recent election and southern slave-holding states leaving the Union because of that election. Every traveler had an opinion. Those sympathetic to the South claimed the North drove them to it by meddling in Southern affairs. Some sympathetic to the North were happy to see slave holding states secede while others wanted war. When I left Missouri, six states had seceded from the Union. By the time I arrived in Colorado, that number had reached eleven.

Frequently we played music around the fire. I had the jaw harp, and Jake had a mouth organ. Others would join in with whatever instrument they had brought or would just sit and sing along. Occasionally we would run into someone who was talented with a fiddle, and the night became lively. Always at least one person would stand guard outside the fire to watch for danger. It was a job I hated, but I performed my share of the watches and spent many a day walking half asleep and disappointed in again missing a full night's slumber.

As often as time would allow, I found time to write in my journal or draw sketches of my journey.

Wednesday, April 3, 1861 day 3

Three days into this venture, I am farther from home than I have ever been. I am still in the state of Missouri, and we now follow the Osage River Road that will lead to the Santa Fe Trail. There is more traffic on the road than I would have imagined, and many are heading west to find gold. Wagons pass us with great frequency, mostly heading to the City of Kansas, Santa Fe, or beyond. We have to leave the trail for some distance to find places to sleep with ample grazing for the animals.

I am surprised by the number of wagons being pulled by teams of oxen. I would have guessed that in these times, everyone but me would travel with horses or mules. These oxen seem to do well on the trail, and it is said that when water is scarce these animals perform better than horses. A good number of men are pulling handcarts, sometimes in the company of their wives and children. No one but me is traveling in the company of a team of donkeys. I am humbled, but I travel with a great deal more ease than those with these small handcarts. I wonder how anyone can pull his supplies over such a great distance, but I understand that many Mormons traveled even farther with these handcarts when they moved to the Great Salt Desert.

Sunday, April 7, 1861 day 7

Though today is Sunday and we probably should have made this a day of rest, we managed to travel about fifteen miles.

The towns we pass through seem to be getting smaller and farms are getting farther apart and we may now be in Kansas Territory. We are on the famous Santa Fe Trail. There are many others journeying to the gold fields. Those on horseback or with teams of horses pulling wagons pass us hourly. We frequently pass men pulling handcarts with very few provisions. We travel about the same speed as the ox-drawn wagons.

Why did I not think to travel with an ox-drawn cart? Mrs. Hultgren had to sell her milk cow when she moved and she left two old wagon wheels in her barn. I could have made a cart to carry me and some of my supplies. That cow, no doubt, would have dried up from the walk, but I could have sold or butchered her when I got to the gold fields. My feet hurt from all this walking.

Jake and I have been joined by two Irishmen. These brothers, Sean and Paddy Donohoo, have asked to join us as they have heard that Indians are less likely to strike large groups. Both Sean and Paddy are walking, and each is leading a horse packed with about two hundred pounds of supplies, including four clay jugs of whiskey tied loosely to the side of each horse. They have been in America only five years and have walked sixteen hundred miles from Boston. They are taking the Santa Fe Trail instead of the more popular Platte River route because they wintered with relatives in a Missouri town near Grass Creek. At the rate they take swigs from those jugs, I doubt that the whiskey will be in those jugs too much longer.

Tuesday, April 16, 1861 day 16

We are definitely into Kansas Territory now. The terrain looks more unfamiliar as there are fewer trees and more grassland. Farms are spaced well apart with fewer tilled fields and more pastureland. Our group is growing, though loosely. As we are getting into less inhabited country, there is security in numbers. Indians are not a problem, but road robbers can be. With the help of Mr. Hultgren's journal, I can tell travelers how far it is to the next water and where to rendezvous. Jake frequently rides ahead with other riders but is always at the proposed spot. By my best estimating we make twelve to sixteen miles a day. Unlike what that fifteen year old journal states, there is precious little firewood and almost no game at each stop. Some evenings we must content ourselves with beef jerky and cold biscuits for supper. Holly gets the same but smaller portions.

Thursday, April 18, 1861, day 18

We are now over two hundred miles from Grass Creek and the countryside looks very little like Missouri. Sometimes we can walk for more than an hour without seeing a single tree. We just observe mile upon mile of tall prairie grass covering mile upon mile of gently rolling hills.

Today Holly seemed nervous as we walked and frequently turned around to sniff the air behind us. I worried that we were being followed by highwaymen intent on stealing our money, while Jake worried that we were being followed by Indians intent on stealing our scalps. Whatever was causing Holly to be so nervous caused us great anxiety, as well, and we carried our weapons as we walked for fear of an ambush.

In late afternoon we stopped at a campsite by a little spring already occupied by nearly twenty other travelers and were thankful for the safety that such a number of armed men would provide.

We had scarcely begun to unload our animals when Jake yelled, "Look!" and pointed to the setting sun. On a hill about a quarter of a mile away stood a lone figure on horseback. Neither he nor the horse moved a muscle.

"Indians!" someone yelled and at least a dozen of us grabbed our weapons and pointed towards that lone horseman. Those with spy glasses tried to get a better look, but the sun totally obscured their view. All they could say was that he probably was indeed an Indian because he was riding bareback and that he had the body of a boy in his teens. "If he's alone, that Injun boy is harmless as an old coon dog!" a man from Ohio yelled, "look at that gimp arm"

The young man and his horse remained motionless for what seemed like an eternity but was probably only about a minute. He then raised his right arm high up and continued to remain frozen as a statue.

The lone woman in our group was very frightened and cried out, "Why doesn't someone just shoot him!"

I put my scattergun back in its place on Eve's pack and walked about twenty paces towards the Indian against the warnings of Jake and the others. I raised my right arm as if to salute him back and remained there motionless myself.

For about half a minute I held my arm up as did the Indian until he turned on his horse and disappeared behind the hill. I then turned and returned in silence to unpack my animals.

"Do you know that Indian?" Jake asked me.

"I hope so, Jake," I responded. "I certainly hope so."

Saturday, April 20, 1861 day 20

Spring has definitely arrived and the days are warm but not hot. Walking has become easy and we now average nearly twenty miles a day. Jake would gladly double that distance, as he is riding, but does not complain too much. My feet are well calloused and the animals are in good condition but the twenty miles seems to be a good pace. The Donohoos agree.

Sunday, April 22, 1861 day 22

Today it rained all day. Being the Sabbath we decided to rest ourselves and our animals. We are stopped at a site Mr. Hultgren referred to as Oak Creek Crossing. It has plenty of firewood, ample grass for the animals and is a pleasant refuge from the Kansas wind except for the drizzle. I shot two rabbits. Jake and I roasted them slowly over a spit with a few remaining onions and had a rare and delicious noon time meal. Holly also had a rare and possibly delicious meal of rabbit entrails and bones. All in all, it was a peaceful and relaxing day, despite the rain.

Tuesday, April 24,1861 day 24

Our group now numbers ten: Jake and I, plus the two Irishmen, Sean and Paddy, and a group of six we met the day of the rains at Oak Creek Crossing. They are from Indiana and not much older than I. They include the Watts brothers, Isaiah and Kaiden, who are sawyers. They have a sturdy wagon full of not only food and grain but saws, axes and hardware of which I have never seen the like. Being pulled by two oxen is a large iron contraption on steel wheels.

"Is that a steam engine?" I asked for I had only heard of but never seen such a thing.

Kaiden nodded, "We're off to the mountains to supply the gold seekers with timber, where we hear that more money can be made 'mining the miners' than can be made looken for gold."

"But why the steam engine?" I asked. "Are there no streams to power a sawmill?"

"This is 1861, not 1681. The future is here, and we're taking it west with us!" replied Isaiah sarcastically.

With them are their friends: Otis, Floyd, Earl, and Otto. The latter four are all sons of immigrant farmers and speak to each other in German and talk to us in slow, deliberate English. Each walks beside a well packed horse or mule. They share one small ox-drawn wagon in which they carry their cooking and camping supplies, and they take turns driving that wagon. Starting two weeks before Jake and me, these Indiana men have already covered five hundred miles to our three hundred.

Thursday, April 25, 1861 day 25

About three hours ago we chose a good camp site protected from the wind with nearby water and bluffs from which to stand watch. I did not have to hunt for meat tonight as I was able to shoot a grouse that I scared up when I left the trail a few hours ago. I cooked it over the fire, fed Holly the bones, and now have an hour of daylight left in which to write.

As I start writing, a wagon train of freighters has pulled up to our site. Wagon trains are always welcome as this means more protection from Indians and perhaps a little news from back east, but this train is quite different from others we have met as it is larger and more organized. There are more freight wagons than usual, eight instead of the usual two to four. All are pulled by eight mules or horses instead of the usual two to four. I cannot identify the cargo, but judging from the voices of the drivers, this train is from one of the remaining southern states. What really makes this train different from other caravans is not its size or the eight mounted and armed riders; it is different because four colored slaves were walking behind as they approached. Walking is not really the right word; these poorly dressed and shoeless wretches are forced to keep up with the brisk pace of the wagons. All the white men ride horses or drive the wagons. With the exception of an old colored man driving the cook wagon, all slaves are forced to keep up on foot.

I have rarely seen a Negro other than Mason or Auntie Martha in my life, and know of no one who owns another person as a slave. I have only seen these dark skinned people as they pass through Grass Creek on their way to or from St. Louis on business. We are now in Kansas Territory, which is a free territory, but there is no law preventing the use of slaves as long as they are needed in the trading of goods. I do not hold, as some suggest, that coloreds are the same as white folks in every way but skin color. Nevertheless, I am bothered that these four dark men receive less care than we give our animals. After what I am sure was a grueling day of trotting in the dust of the wagons, they must now set up camp and toil for these traders. I am told that a couple of years ago there were a series of debates in Illinois that caught the attention of the nation between Senator Douglas and Abraham Lincoln when they ran against each other for a Senate seat. Mr. Douglas asserted that slaves were descended from a cursed son of Noah named Ham. Apparently his children and his children's children would be forever scorned. Does this justify slavery? I searched my Bible for an hour this evening to find this passage but could not find it. I know that King David, Abraham, King Saul and others had slaves, or servants. I remember that Moses led his people out of slavery. Why does one passage in the Bible about a banished tribe mean that these coloreds have to run in filth just for the opportunity to wait on some so-called "Southern gentlemen?"

Friday, April 26, 1861 day 26

This morning the freight wagons left an hour before we did. The slaves arose early and had fed and watered the horses before daybreak. These men not only work their slaves hard but drive their animals from sunrise to sunset leaving little time for rest.

As I was preparing my breakfast, I overheard a conversation much like this:

"Blacky, I heard some rumbling in the kegs on Evert's wagon. Go and re-tie them."

The slave answered, "Yassa Mr. Fletcher" and quickly ran to the wagon, pulled off the canvas and tightened the ropes securing at least twenty wooden kegs. It was then that I suspected that this group of men was in a hurry to get Kentucky Bourbon to the gold fields. Otis had tried to make conversation with them but a curt "Kaintuck" was all he got when he asked one where they were from. Bourbon would also explain the heavy guard.

"Boy, bring me more coffee," another asked a different slave, and that slave trotted to the fire to retrieve the pot.

With the exception of the old colored cook, whom they called "Cookie," all slaves were addressed simply as "Blacky, Darky, or Boy." As they were about to leave Cookie spoke up, "Might da boys ride?"

The apparent leader of the caravan shook his head. "They know their punishment."

I have no idea what the infraction was, but I bet it was minor when compared to the punishment of running behind those wagons.

At times I felt like my father's slave on the farm, for I did not get paid, but I rode in the buggy when we went places and I always had good food and decent clothing. I knew that I was loved and wanted for more than just what labor I could provide. I really did not "slave" for my father, I toiled with him and he always seemed to work harder than I did.

I shall quit this journal for tonight and do more Bible research. Perhaps I will find my answer and write more tomorrow.

Saturday, April 27, 1861 day 27

I have now read my Bible until the sun went completely down and again by candlelight for another two or three hours for two straight evenings and found almost nothing to justify my feelings of pity for those five pathetic slaves. I am still angry with those slave holders for their cruelty, but it seems that the Bible does indeed close its eyes on the issue of slavery. I found references to slavery and servitude throughout both Testaments of the Bible but found no single place where it was condemned. Moses led his people out of slavery and yet had servants himself. The Ten Commandments even have reference to slavery as in "thou shalt not covet thy neighbor's …manservant." There are numerous places telling us how to treat a servant or to be a good servant, but nowhere could I find a reference to ease my disgust. Am I just jealous that I do not own a slave to do my work as Otis has suggested? I hope not. I just feel that slavery is wrong.

I did find these passages in the New Testament. "Do unto others as you would have them do unto you." "If you have two cloaks and your neighbor has none, then you shall give your neighbor a cloak." I am sure this verse applies to shoes as well. I wish I could have given those poor black skinned men some of my extra clothing; perhaps a handkerchief to keep the dust out of their mouths as they ran.

I'm not sure where the colored man's place is, but the phrase "all men are created equal" is in our Declaration of Independence. If we think that "equal" only applies to white men, then perhaps we should send coloreds to their own territory, just like we are trying to send Indians to their own place. Then we can all truly be equal, and Indians and coloreds can be equal in their own lands. Or maybe if we do continue to condone slavery we should require that those in charge treat their servants with more compassion and give them proper food, clothing and perhaps a ride in the wagon. I am embarrassed that Missouri is a slave-holding state.

When it comes to the Bible, it seems that there are two kinds of people: those who read it for inspiration and those who quote it to justify their opinions. I hope that I am one of the readers. I think that Mr. Douglas, a million slave holders, and perhaps many of the people I know in Grass Creek, including my father, may fall in the latter group. I shall be careful not to quote the Bible if I find myself in an argument for I am beginning to think that quotes can be found for both sides of any dispute.

Sunday, April 28, 1861 day 28

Today is another day of rain and drizzle, and as this is Sunday, we chose to make this a day of rest instead of trying to negotiate a muddy peril. There are no trees to camp under for there are now precious few trees on this grassy plain.

As I sit here in my tent with nothing to do but think or write, my mind wanders not so much to my future which is four hundred miles to the west but to my past which is now four hundred miles to the east.

I think of home frequently and sometimes feel as if I am dragging a very long rope attached to my parents and that farm in Missouri. I don't know why, but sometimes it feels as if Becky Thompson is tugging on that tether. The farther I am from home, the heavier the rope of the past becomes. I think often of how my father is disappointed with my decision to travel west. At times he seemed down-right angry that I even considered a different life than the one he planned for me. His wish was to expand that farm with my help, and by leaving I am not honoring those wishes, an act he probably sees as defiance.

As this is almost May, the plowing should be about finished, and planting may be starting. Brother Michael is now likely to be doing my share of the labor and at age thirteen he will have to yoke up Edna and work in the fields in my place. I feel guilty for causing Michael to endure extra work because of my disinterest in such labor. I also remember that I followed Edna when I was twelve, but I feel guilty nevertheless.

I keep thinking of Becky, for her rope seems to tug at my heart. I only know five girls my age and have never thought of any of them as being more than just a girl of my age. Becky always seemed a little more special as she lived so close and we played together as children. As the years passed we sometimes rode horses, went fishing or just talked with each other as our parents visited. The walks home from church in the weeks before I left were very special. Something about seeing Becky in that dress as I was leaving Grass Creek just sticks in my mind, and on a rainy day such as this my mind does not have much to do but to wander back to the green rolling plains of Missouri and that pleasant girl in the blue dress with a basket of cookies. I wish she were here holding my hand as we walk. I want to kiss her again.

Is my father's opinion of this adventure accurate? Is this quest just another folly of my youth? Am I indeed trying to make my life better, or am I just off on a foolish escapade?

I have another rope pulling on me from the West. This rope is the pull of the mountains and the adventure I shall find; it is the pull of gold and the riches I intend to reap. So far, the rope pulling me lessens the burden of the one I am dragging. Though I sometimes want to turn around, I shall keep plodding forth to find those riches that I truly deserve. I sometimes wish I could share these feelings of regret with my traveling companions but they might scoff at my worries. I will content myself with just my writing in this log. I wish Becky were here. She would listen.

Wednesday, May 1, 1861 day 31

We are meeting more and more "go-backers." Some have turned around because of a tragedy, some have been robbed and have not the means to go on, but many have made it to Colorado, only to find that the gold was not easy to obtain and gave up. Many tell us that there is no gold; that the newly called "Colorado Gold Rush" was a hoax to sell books such as Jake's Smith and Oaks book. These travelers look nearly starved, and many are walking with only what they can carry or with pull carts hauling only meager amounts of food and gear. They come in groups for protection, and we sometimes camp with them. I always provide food for I still have ample and I am thankful to have a large camp for it means more safety from Indians. Holly sleeps by my side to warn me if these "Go Backers" are up to no good, and we both sleep close to my donkeys, gear, and loaded musket. At least one from our group is on watch at all times for it is rumored that "Go Backers" are desperate and can be as vicious as Indians. We have not seen any Indians to date other than that lone boy on a distant hill but have seen dozens who have "seen the elephant."

Thursday, May 2, 1861 day 32

Today we left the Santa Fe Trail and are now on the path known as "The Smoky Hill Route." We have talked about this short cut for weeks. The Watts brothers purchased a map in Indiana of this trail, and by scaling it with my ruler, I figure the path is three hundred miles in a direction straight towards the gold fields. By staying on our current path, we have almost four hundred miles to go, and much of it heads southwest instead of the westerly direction to Pike's Peak. Wagon masters heading to Denver warn us to not venture off the well established Santa Fe Trail. They tell us that travelers on that trail are more likely to get lost, robbed, or scalped. Jake was persistent in convincing us of the need to shave a week off of our travel. Grass and game should be much easier to find when we are on this much less traveled course.

Sunday, May 5, 1861 day35

We are now almost five hundred miles from Grass Creek and two thirds complete with our journey. There are few trees to be seen from this trail. An occasional solitary tree can sometimes be seen in the distance, but mostly the landscape is just hill after hill of a knee high brownish-colored grass. Each mile looks much like the previous mile and water is scarce. Each time we traverse over a hill, I hope to see signs of mountains or the Arkansas River but all I see are more miles and miles of this endless plain.

CHAPTER 4

The Mountain Man

Monday, May 6, 1861 day 36

This morning we saw the darndest sight. Two wagons, escorted by six mounted riders, passed us. Each wagon was pulled by two mules and each rider was armed with a musket at his side. One wagon was heavily packed with provisions including not only food and supplies, but furniture, a piano and finery. In the other wagon were six young women between the ages of twenty and thirty years sitting on various crates and boxes. I suspect that these "ladies" were not ladies at all, but working girls of the "soiled dove" variety. Instead of being attractive "dance hall girls" as described in dime novels, these doves all seemed to possess very unfortunate looks. Only one or two had a full mouth of teeth and three were plump or downright fat. A toothless one seemed to recognize Jake, but he avoided looking at her. Jake has often bragged that he has been with two women but won't say with whom or when. As they passed us by, I saw Jake longing after them. I think that those travelers were from Independence and at least one of them may have provided Jake's often bragged about experiences. I think only lonely creatures would ever pay for the company of a member of the opposite gender, and I am proud to be one of the not-so-lonely. I will have to admit that I think about Becky Thompson frequently, and I think thoughts I never dreamed of before.

An hour later we stopped at a trading post not listed in the Smith and Oaks book or on the Smokey Hill Route map. This was a pleasant surprise, for Jake is nearly out of supplies. Most stores listed on maps are in cities such as St. Louis, Independence or Denver City, but this one is in the middle of this Great American Desert and hundreds of miles from any other store or trading post. The store was built near a camp site on the map referred to as Little Rabbit Spring. Not a tree is to be seen for miles, and the spring is no more than a trickle. What little water springs forth is contained in a hand dug hole and is fenced off. Access can be made only by entering the fenced area surrounding the store. A sign had been painted with charcoal on the outside of the store—

GRIZZLY HATCH'S EMPORIAM

TRADING POST, WAGGIN REPARE,
BLACKSMITH & WATEREN HOLE

The store is no more than a large windowless hut built of sod and rocks and appeared to be built more for defense against Indians than for selling goods. There was a sod barn attached right to the house for keeping animals. A freight wagon was securely chained to a post to prevent theft. A crude sort of jack for lifting wagons had been made of two large wooden poles resting on two large rocks. A bucket of grease was laying on the ground near a fire pit apparently used as a forge. Nothing was outside the store that could be stolen except for about a hundred young chickens in a fenced area. Why a need for that many chickens, I do not know. The hen house was separate from the store but could be secured at night with a latch bolted shut. We might have passed right by, but Jake was low on supplies, and the rest of us were curious what lay inside this strange little building.

Walking inside, we found a store very unlike those in Grass Creek. There was little light except for what came through two small openings, high on each wall. I would not call these windows for they had no glass. The floor was dirt and was packed tight by all the foot traffic and was well swept and tidy. I suspect that ox blood had been poured on the dirt to make it hard, dark, and shiny. We cautiously walked around and found a short paunchy man about sixty years old standing at a tall wooden counter. He was wearing buckskin clothes and a hat made of a badger pelt with the skull still intact. He was the lord of this dark room packed not with boxes and cans but with sacks of grain, flour and jerky. Lying on the floor and on top of these sacks were dry goods such as boots, blankets, rope, gun powder and axle grease but not much else except for a few items Mr. Hatch had traded with the Indians for, such as buffalo robes, dried buffalo meat and leather moccasins. Prices were marked on the items with charcoal and most everything was two to five times more expensive than similar ware in Grass Creek. Jake wished to purchase a bag of corn meal and offered two dollars instead of the asking price of five. Mr. Hatch countered his offer with "Five dollars or go to Hell." Jake then called him a 'greedy old scoundrel' and Mr. Hatch quickly presented a large and intimidating knife and pointed towards the door. No one until then had even noticed a knife, but Mr. Hatch was obviously always prepared for trouble. Jake backed up two steps and apologized. He then bought the five dollar bag, as he is nearly out of food and a half bag of oats for three dollars, as well. I looked at some moccasins and was tempted to buy them. They look more comfortable for walking than my heavy boots, but I did not give in to the temptation, for two dollars is twice what I would pay Cobbler Watkins for a new pair of boots, and I may need my money later.

Jake, angry about the knife incident, waited outside, but the rest of us lingered, all fascinated by the Indian trading goods. Mr. Hatch had put his knife away and was pleasant and played the part of an aging mountain man to a tee. He used his musket as a cane, spat a lot, and told stories. As a trapper and scout he had traveled with the likes of Jim Bridger and Kit Carson, the two famous explorers and Indian fighters from Missouri. While trapping for The Hudson Bay Company he encountered great bears at a place where sulfur and steam boiled out of the ground and chose the name Grizzly after killing one of these great bears. He had been to the gold fields in 1859 as a freight hauler but found more profit freighting his goods only part way and selling provisions to travelers. Anticipating this great rush he built this store from sod and rocks last spring away from all civilization with the knowledge that many would need to re-supply by this time. Mr. Hatch now lives in the store with his Indian wife and dog and leaves only infrequently to either the city of Kansas or Santa Fe for trade goods or to Denver City to sell some of these wares.

Mr. Hatch commented on my donkeys saying, "Nice burro train boy; you should do well in the mountains." I had never heard the word "burro" before. He says it means donkey in Spanish and, to me, that word sounds a whole lot more noble than donkey or ass. He told me that a sure footed burro can carry goods where no horse is able to venture. This surprised me, for until now I have been ashamed of my lack of a horse. I shall refer to my six beasts of burden as burros from now on for I have come to respect them and their ability to travel all day with a load on their backs.

He also noticed the Watts' wagons and the wood cutting tools. "Why the steam engine?" he asked.

"This is 1861, not 1681. The future is here, and we're taking it west with us!" replied Isaiah in the same tone of voice he used when I first asked.

Mr. Hatch fixed his eyes on me and offered: "I saw you eying those fine Apache moccasins. Chop wood for me for the rest of the day and I shall give them to you for only one dollar." He then offered each of the others anything worth a dollar off the asking price for a half day of labor chopping wood. As there is no firewood for miles, Mr. Hatch can sell firewood for enormous profits. With the exception of Jake, who was still outside, we all agreed. There were still a few hours of daylight left and Jake wanted to travel on. He stewed for a while, and then packed his mule, mounted his horse and yelled, "See you in the gold fields!" We tried to talk him out of leaving, but he was still angry about the knife incident and angry with us for our willingness to stay the rest of the day to work for Mr. Hatch. With no idea of how to find us in the gold fields, he rode off. I am sorry to see him leave. We all are.

Old Tom

Jake had been my good friend since we learned to read together in school and I valued his company. He had always been impatient and he had often made rash decisions, but this time his impatience had lead to his rashest decision. I suspected that he was in a hurry to catch that wagon load of prostitutes. We all watched in wonder as he rode off. The most unprepared of us all was now traveling alone in a very inhospitable country.

I am now lying on a bed of soft hay writing in this journal with a lamp hanging above my head on a secure beam. We chopped wood for a few hours and instead of buying the moccasins, I just took a half bag of beans for my labor. We were about to continue on to find a place to camp when Mr. Hatch said, "You may sleep in the barn if you each buy something." Jake had already bought the grain, but as he was now gone, that didn't contribute to the deal. The dollar's worth of supplies we had each earned didn't count either, so I bought two eggs and a piece of bacon as did each of the other eight. Each item cost two cents, the same price an entire breakfast costs at the hotel in Grass Creek, but well worth the money. Tonight we shall sleep on soft hay instead of the hard ground. No one will have to stay awake on watch, and in the morning we shall dine like kings.

I worry about Jake. I understand his eagerness to move faster, but I hope that he can soon realize his foolishness to travel alone and perhaps rejoin us again.

Old Tom

The next day turned out to be one of the most memorable of my journey, and though it all happened fifty years ago, I remember it as if it happened last month:

For the first time since I left Missouri I had a full night's sleep. We had no worry of Indians, robbers or bad weather for we were safely latched inside the barn with our animals. As the barn had no windows, we awoke well rested after sun-up with Mr. Hatch pounding on the door. "Go get some coffee boys," he shouted. We scrambled to find the door, but it was completely dark inside. Because we were inside and warm for the first time in a month, we were dressed only in our union suits and were still putting on our trousers when Patrick unbolted the door. The sun had been up for an hour and Mrs. Hatch was in the yard with a breakfast fire burning. She had already baked biscuits and had a pot of steaming coffee and offered to cook our bacon and eggs. We obliged her.

While we were eating, Mr. Hatch hitched up his freighter to two very large gray mules. Next to the wagon were two whiskey barrels he had uncovered from some hidden location.

"You boys gonna die of thirst soon without these barrels."

"No thankee," Paddy politely responded and showed him his old army canteen and a couple of clay jugs tied to his saddle.

Mr. Hatch laughed and spat on the dry dusty ground.

"The last hundred miles is dry as a parched buffalo skull, and you do not carry more water than can be drunk in half a day. Buzzards will love to pick on your scraggly bones."

"I see no price charcoaled on those old barrels," I said.

"Not fer sale," he replied punctuating his remark with another spit. "You have to work for 'em."

We did not know about the lack of water, but we had noticed that with each passing day, water was becoming more and more scarce. The Smoky Hill River that we were following was now no more that a muddy trickle, and we still had two hundred miles to go. Surely he knew what he was talking about.

"We ain't a choppen no more wood," Kaiden said.

"Hop on," he said and pointed to the freighter.

"You want us to miss out on a day's travel just for two worthless empty kegs?" asked Isaiah.

"Work or die.....Yore choice"

We discussed the situation out of earshot of Mr. Hatch and agreed that if we had to go more than a few hours without water, we would run out. Until now we had always found water for the animals and carried only enough for us to drink as we walked. Reluctantly we hopped on the wagon.

We then rode with him ten miles to the nearest grove of trees to fell them for firewood. The Watts brothers proved to be masters at cutting timber and Mr. Hatch was pleased. It was hard work, but we were glad to do it for we found this old mountain man to be fascinating and we needed a break from the monotony of our travels. Our animals needed a break as well, and for the first time in a month we were able to remove their halters and let them freely graze in a fenced pasture.

As we rode to the grove Mr. Hatch told stories with his cultured dialect. What few mountain men I ever met talked in a similar style. Words and names were abbreviated: beavers became beeves, Santa

59

Fe became Fe, Grizzly bear was Griz and so on. A typical sentence might be: "We rode hard and follered those injuns for two days with no grub." He would then punctuate his words with a spit. Some stories I believed, and some I didn't, such as his story of the place we now call Yellowstone where water and mud boiled out of the ground with a smell of rotten eggs and the sound of a distant steamboat. He got serious with us at one point and gave us advice for staying alive for the remaining two hundred miles of our journey, nearly all of which was to be in Indian country.

Tuesday, May 7, 1861 day 37

I am again writing in the comfort of a dry barn as today we did not travel westward but spent a day working for an old fur trapper named Grizzly Hatch. He has been in the West for years and gave us good advice. I shall write his rules down as best as I can remember and memorize this advice.

"This is Injun country and has been forever. Respect the red man and you will get respected back. A Plains Indian will gladly kill you, but will not put his life at unnecessary risk to do so. He respects your firepower but might wait in ambush if he suspects that your guard is down."

1. Always have your musket or scatter gun within arm's reach and loaded. Indians may also possess weapons but will seldom attack unless the odds are overwhelmingly in their favor.

2. Do not ride or walk in a single file manner as Indians will wait for you to pass and then attack from the rear. It is best to cluster together.

3. Never wander off the trail alone to hunt or gather. If hunting, only one person should take a shot and all others must keep their arms ready, for while you are loading your weapons an Indian may have six arrows in the air heading for your heart.

4. Never walk straight up a hill for you don't know what might be crouching at the top. An Indian has the patience a white man cannot comprehend. If you do walk around that hill, be wary of the next one for they are quick and silent.

5. Do not build large fires. Not only will the sight and smell attract Indians, your vision will be impaired. They see you, but you cannot see them and you will be easy to shoot arrows at. A good fire is a small one made of buffalo chips as dung not only burns with a slow bluish flame, it emits little smoke or odor.

6. Keep your horses and food close to you. Stealing from or just touching the enemy is called a "coup" and is revered as a sign of bravery. An Indian counts his coup and boasts of them to his fellow warriors. The more coups an Indian has, the longer he can brag of them in council and Indians listen intently while another warrior recounts his bravery. If your horses are far from where you or your guards are, an Indian may quietly lead your animal away, be content with his coup and you won't know that your horse is gone until the next morning.

7. Trust your dog. A dog's nose will awaken it with the smell of an unknown intruder.

Then he said the darndest thing: "I can tell by looking in your eyes that you have been eating biscuits and meat and no fruits or greens. You will get weak soon, and may not have the strength to look for gold; then your teeth'll fall out." He showed us which prairie weeds we could pick to boil for tea and which ones we could eat. We recognized the dandelions and had heard that some people eat them, but no matter whether you boil, fry or eat them raw, I am sure that they taste awful.

After a day of hard labor cutting firewood, we all hopped on top of the wood for a ride back to the store. This time instead of advice, Mr. Hatch told stories of his life as a mountain man. I shall recount one such tale in his words, as best as I can remember.

"I was a scout for Colonel Kearney's Army during the War with the Mesicans. I was all alone out there on a gray mare right in the heart of Navahoo country armed only with two loaded Hawkens en my skinnen knife. I seen out the corner of my eye Injuns, a dozen of 'em, all red as blood en angry as a rabid coon. They was all mounted on painted ponies en all carrying bows en arries. Their horses was snorting fire, en kicking dust as they was chargen right at me. I kicked that ol' mare, White Star, in the ribs en galloped up the canyon with no ideer of where I was a headed. The Injuns galloped after me like they was rushen from the devil hisself. The harder I rode, the closer the Indians came but I kept ridin, not bothering to shoot for I would surely just waste my shot. The more I rode, the narrower the canyon got en the closer those injuns came. After an hour of hard riding I found myself plum square at the end of a box canyon with nowhere to go but straight up the red sandstone cliffs. I jumped off Ol' White Star at a gallop en skittered up the rock wall, but those Injuns had dismounted also en were climbin after me, en they could climb like burnin squirrels. I found a rock to hide behind en took careful aim with my Hawkens, but they was nowhere to be seen for they was behind rocks themselves en shootin arries into the sky 'til the sun was blotted out."

Then he stopped talking and spat his punctuation onto the dust below. We all just stared waiting for the next word but he said nothing. Finally Paddy Donohoo asked, "so what happened next?"

"Why they kilt me en took my scalp!" he joked, and took off his badger head cap to show us his bald head.

He went right in to his next story of being chased by a grizzly bear up a pine tree. When he got to the part where the Griz was eating the trunk of the tree to make the tree fall, he stopped his story again with a sloppy spit. This time no one said a thing.

Finally Kaiden Watts said, "I think that an old pine tree must have been a tastier meal than a long dead mountain man." This time we all had the laugh.

All in all it was a fine day, and I shall never forget it or Grizzly Hatch.

Old Tom

After another safe night in the barn we awoke refreshed and ready to travel on. We checked each others faces closely to see if our morning cup of dandelion tea had changed our eyes. The old mountain man was so pleased with our work that he gave us a two dollar discount on anything in his store. I put on those two dollar Apache moccasins and strutted proudly as a prairie rooster. Paddy Donohoo had a new knife sheathed to his side. Isaiah Watts covered his load with his new Navajo blanket. The others all had food or grain.

I suspect that at two dollars off the asking price Mr. Hatch still made a handsome profit but we didn't care. I know that I didn't, for I had that fine pair of Apache moccasins. It took only a few miles to realize that my sturdy boots were more suited to the rutted trail but I kept those moccasins for years and proudly wore them as house slippers. Many years later when burning trash, I discovered them in with all the household debris. I retrieved them smoldering, but still in fine shape and wore them proudly about the house again to the dismay of my wife.

In the last few years, Wild West Shows have come through the area, and I always take my family to see the horsemanship and shooting. In these shows there frequently is an old man dressed in buckskin clothing, telling stories, spitting, and shooting. These old men may or may not have been real fur trappers, Indian fighters, or scouts, but I enjoy this part of the show the best, for at one brief time in my life, I knew Grizzly Hatch, Mountain Man.

CHAPTER 5

Elephants on the Trail

Wednesday, May 8, 1861 day 38

Today I saw my first buffalo. I did not shoot it for it was already dead. Then I saw another, and another, and then four more; all dead, all skinned, and all left to rot. They did not smell, and there were few flies for I think they were all freshly killed within the day. These animals appeared to be much like oxen only larger. As all this buffalo was still fresh and would otherwise go to waste, we each cut out a few pounds of the choicest meat and set up camp early to cook us up a feast. I cut my meat into a thick steak for tonight, and the rest into very thin strips to soak in salt brine. I shall enjoy these strips along the trail as they dry into a chewable and tasty jerky. For Holly I cut some fleshy bones. These I will tie to Cain and Abel at the rear of the train to dry in the sun. If they begin to smell, no one will be near to be offended. Holly will have plenty to keep her busy at nights from now on.

As it was still daylight, we had no one on guard when Holly started barking. Quickly we all grabbed our muskets or scatter guns and held to the ready as we watched a lone figure walk towards us. Holly quit barking before any of us recognized the traveler. Paddy yelled out in his Irish brogue, "I be damned, it's Jake!"

Jake walked slowly and humbly into our campsite. We were all full of questions, but Jake just sat by the fire and stared at it. I feared that he had seen the "elephant." It was evident that something had happened to his horse and mule. I asked if he was hungry. He nodded and I gave him a piece of buffalo meat, two biscuits, and a cup of dandelion tea. As he ate, he began talking.

"It took only three hours to catch the wagon load of women and the six riders. They had stopped to camp for the night when I rode up. Six muskets were pointed at me as I dismounted. 'Are you looking for another escort?' I asked. No one said anything until a man about thirty-five years old, and possibly the leader said, 'We need all the guns we can get. Ride with us till the Arkansas meets the mountains but not a foot farther.'"

"I was eager to get to the gold fields," Jake said, "and this group appeared to cover twice the distance in a day than we do. Besides, traveling with a load of ladies might prove to be far more entertaining than trudging along with the likes of you."

He attempted a smile at this point, but none of us returned that smirk.

"Where are Muffin and Hay Burner?" we asked.

He said nothing for a few seconds and then continued his story.

"They allowed me to sleep under a wagon that night but not until I pulled the first watch and I had no opportunity to socialize with the 'doves.' While I was on a small bluff on my belly with a ready musket, I could hear the giggling and drunken revelry of the group. In the morning they had a breakfast of apples and salt pork while I ate dried biscuits. We got an early start and moved at a brisk pace for about six hours when one of the riders spotted a distant herd of twelve buffalo about a mile away. We all whooped and hollered and at once rode hard towards the animals. It was our intention to get on the far side of them, herd them towards the wagons and shoot them. We positioned ourselves on the far side of the herd, flapped our arms, whistled, and yelled, but the buffalo were unimpressed. They continued grazing as if we were not there, and we could have shot them all right then. I figured they might move if I made a bigger noise, so I shot my musket into the air. The buffalo started running at stampede pace straight towards the wagons. We immediately gave chase and started shooting and didn't down a single animal for half a mile. The harder we rode, the faster they charged. The herd continued directly for the wagons, and we couldn't steer them away. They crashed right into them and then slowed as they neared this ravine. It was then that we were able to shoot six of them. Most took more than one bullet before falling.

"We first went back to assess the mess left by the stampede. The 'doves' were frightened but unhurt. The wagons had been rammed but remained largely intact. One mule was limping, but it looked only bruised, so there was very little damage for what could have been a disaster.

"The leader of the group, whose name I now knew as Milo, then insisted that we all skin the newly killed animals because the hides could come in useful for their business, though I doubt he knew how to tan a hide or properly care for one. We all had knives and set out at once to skin all six buffalo. Though I knew nothing, some of the others had been farmers and knew how to remove a beef hide and with their instruction a bearded man named Zeke and I removed two hides

66

while the others, in pairs of two, skinned the other four. We dragged the hides to the camp site, rubbed salt on the fleshy side and tied them over the tops of the wagons to dry in the sun. It was getting dark and time to eat, but once again I found that it was my duty to perform the first watch. Like the night before I found a bluff from which to do guard duty while they, again, feasted and drank over a fire much larger than we ever allow.

"At day break we ate a fine breakfast of braised buffalo meat and coffee. I saddled up Muffin and packed my provisions on Hay Burner while the others saddled up and hitched their wagons. I was ready for the first time since we left Missouri to travel a respectable distance of 30 to 50 miles when I heard Milo yelling. 'This Goddam mule's leg is broke and the fool who started that stampede just traded me his mule for this one!'

"Everyone looked at me. He walked up to me and pointed his musket at my nose. 'Remove your saddle,' he demanded and I removed the pack from old Hay Burner… What else could I do? I think that he would have shot me if I didn't. Zeke led Hay Burner to his place at a wagon and hitched him up. I then packed what provisions I could load on Muffin and left the rest on the ground. I was now a foot traveler, just like you and the rest, and could never keep up with this group, so I resigned myself to walking. Milo had taken his mule off the trail a ways and we all watched as he put his musket to the animal's ear and shot. The mule fell, and in a great rage, Milo approached me. He again pointed the musket at my nose. I let go of Muffin's reins and he then pointed his musket to the right of my ear and fired. This action startled Muffin and she took off running. Milo said 'Git your horse' and I started walking. I wandered north for miles and then started making circles in the hope that Muffin had tired and was now looking for me. I walked all day with no food or water, and all I found was you."

"You're lucky you didn't find Indians," I said.

We all were still a little angry with Jake for leaving us behind like he did. But he was my friend and all the others liked him as well; we also felt sorry for him, so we allowed him to stay and share our food and supplies. I even allowed him to have one of my few remaining honey and oat cookies. As he was exhausted and very disheartened, he did not have to perform watch tonight.

Thursday, May 9, 1861 day 39 and a good day

At day's end our trail has come upon a section of the Smoky Hill River where again we have trees and water and game. I do not know why some portions of this river have trees and some do not for back home trees are always abundant near water. I allowed Jake to walk with me and to share in my still bountiful food. He had always ridden at the head of our group in a vain attempt to hurry us along, and now we walked at the lead as a sign of perseverance. As we approached the river Holly left the trail and headed down into the trees. I thought little of her actions as she frequently leaves the trail to chase rabbits or small game. She returned a few minutes later, and following her was Jake's horse Muffin, still saddled and still carrying all Jake's possessions. I gave Jake a handful of oats as Muffin approached. He allowed Muffin to eat for a while and said, "We have gold to find!" and started walking west, with Muffin at his side. Jake, though humbled, did not head home as I would have expected, for apparently the "elephant" he had seen did not defeat his spirit.

"We have gold to find," I said and followed behind him.

Tuesday, May 14, 1861 day 44

Each evening we find a campsite with other travelers as protection from Indian raids. There are travelers from all parts of the country, and I always find tales from other parts of America fascinating. Frequently, however, the talk is of secession and no man can resist taking a side. Tonight I heard that Texas has now left the Union, making it seven states to have seceded since Abraham Lincoln was elected in November. Some from northern states say good riddance to those sinful "secesh" people. Many from the East want the army to invade those states, though for what reason I cannot understand. The thinking of those from the South is that slave holding states had no choice but to secede as Lincoln had vowed to stop slavery and the South cannot exist without that form of labor. Southerners always talk about "states' rights" and respond with anger to any talk of an invasion or abolition of slavery. They say that not a single state south of the Ohio River voted in favor of Mr. Lincoln, and that this election was the final straw on the backs of the Southern economy.

I do not know how to feel about states leaving the Union as I do not agree with slavery, but I do not like the idea of the country splitting apart. If we are to have two countries, I hope that Missouri does not join this new confederacy. Grass Creek is a peaceful farming community with no slaves for miles. Many around those parts are abolitionists and think that the non-slave-holding areas should secede from Missouri, but I doubt that that could ever happen. I am happy to be moving to the gold country, for this area they now call Colorado is a free territory and I shall not have to watch the cruelty associated with human bondage.

Wednesday, May 15, day 45

The day got very hot as the sun beat down on us. Early in the afternoon we came upon what we would call back home a "swimming hole." We did something unusual for us and undressed and hopped into the river, for this rare swimming hole was in a wooded spot where no one could happen upon us and see us. We took turns taking guard. The water was somewhat cold but felt extremely refreshing. We washed our clothing in the cold water and hung them to dry over tree limbs. While we waited for our clothes to dry, we built a fire, caught some small fish, and had a rare midday feast of hot food.

"Look at those puppies!" Kaiden Watts yelled and everyone looked at my calloused feet and laughed. My stockings are all wearing quite thin from all this walking and my feet now are red and hard and look like ox leather. I hope that I can quickly find gold when we get to Pike's Peak and hire some woman to make me a few pairs of good wool socks. Perhaps I can also find a cobbler and hire him to make me some new boots.

Our clothes soon dried in the hot sun, and we journeyed on for another four hours refreshed and clean for the first time in over a month.

Saturday, May 18, 1861 day 48

I am writing about events from last night as I did no writing and sat around the fire for hours, not so much talking, as listening. We had made camp with about twenty other men in a small wooded area by a trickle of water in the nearly dry river. About half of the men were not traveling west to find gold, but east to go home. At sundown we were surprised when a freight wagon approached our camp being driven by a solitary driver and pulled by two large gray mules. We recognized the old mountain man at once—Grizzly Hatch. He is on his way to Denver City with a freighter load of trade goods, and has just covered in three days the same one hundred and fifty miles that has taken us almost two weeks to travel.

We have seen hundreds of freight wagons loaded with dozens of various freight items, but this wagon load was not only interesting, but humorous. Along with other trade goods, Mr. Hatch was transporting about one hundred pullets and young laying hens in about twenty-five wooden crates and two fat sows about ready to give birth in two large crates. He told us that the surest way to transport fresh meat is "alive and birthin." After watering and feeding all his stock he collected about a dozen eggs and tossed them to us. "Where you're headed, boys, these are worth their weight in gold; enjoy 'em."

He brought news that he says is spreading across the country "like a prairie fire." It seems that the South Carolina militia fired on a fort in Charleston harbor, and the Union army surrendered. President

70

Lincoln has called for the northern states to raise a volunteer force of seventy-five thousand troops to quickly put down what he calls an "insurrection," and the Southern states are building armies as well.

In our camp tonight, as any other evening, are men from both the North and the South. Many had already heard the news in Denver and were hurrying home to join those armies. Arguments broke out, and I feared that a war might break out here on the plains of Kansas Territory. No fighting started, but heated words were certainly exchanged.

A former Pennsylvania Militia officer, about thirty years old, boastfully proclaimed, "Once those rebs look down the barrels of seventy-five thousand fine Pennsylvania rifled musket barrels, they'll run like the scared rabbits they are."

A Georgian who had been silent up to this point allowed his anger to boil over and yelled, "I shall look for you on the field of battle, you loud-mouthed Yankee pile of trash!"

Grizzly Hatch held up both hands like a grandfather silencing a dinner table discussion gone wrong, and everyone became quiet. He said, "I have lived long en seen much… No such critter as an 'easy to put down uprisen' when one side wants to punish en one side wants to be left alone. White man has been trying to put down Injun uprisens here fer forty years, en those thar redskins are still thick as bees en twice as ornery."

71

A man who had once been a school teacher in Vermont added, "Those of you who are book learned like to talk about the 'so-called' War for Independence. If you stop to think about it, the British were trying to hold their union together and punish the rebellious colonies with the best army in the world. Look which side won."

A lot of men jeered this comment though some were nodding their heads. Having been jeered at, the teacher sat down and said no more.

Grizzly then stood up. "I hear you dandies singing your songs about 'the land of the free en the home of the brave', en liven en die'n in Dixie, but soon you'll be crying funeral dirges. Shooten en killen ain't so fun when others are shooten en killen you."

He spat and continued, "You'll be lucky if you ain't all buried six feet under by Christmas."

He then turned the talk to something merrier, "What you boys know 'bout wimmen or whiskey?"

Though I did not add even a word to the conversation, it did get merrier with much laughing and plenty of foul talk. Most admitted that they were more familiar with whiskey than women, and it seems most everyone brought whiskey but left a girl behind. I thought a lot about Becky last night.

This morning Mr. Hatch was hitched up and moving before the rest of us had finished breakfast. "Get yore fill of water here fer there ain't no more fer a hunnerd miles. If you cain't foller my tracks just head due west towards that little white speck in the distance."

As he whipped his team he turned his head to us and yelled, "See ya on yore recoil en don't forget to spend that Colorado gold in my trading post."

I thought about his words of last night, all day, as I walked. Why do men seem to enjoy killing one another? Biblical generals were often "smoting" their enemies. I do not even know the meaning of that word, but I always felt that it was a bad way to die. Are we not supposed to love our enemies?

I often reflect on that day two years ago when Father and his church friends rode away in glory to punish that small band of Indian hunters. Their chests were puffed out proudly as they mounted their horses, and I was among those cheering as they galloped away. I keep thinking about that Indian boy my father shot. He seemed little different than any other boy his age other than his appearance. Did he deserve a bullet in his shoulder just because his skin was darker than mine and he wore a feather in his hair? I still hold bad feelings towards Father for hiding behind a rock and shooting this boy.

The groups of men we encounter are heading to their homes to find this same sense of greatness that I can no longer cheer for. I wonder just how long a man can keep his chest puffed out.

I remembered how Jake and I used to pretend to be soldiers holding off great armies of British Red Coats or Indian warriors. We would sit in trees for hours and point our sticks at the imaginary enemy, never missing a shot or losing a battle. With those same sticks over our shoulders, we then pretended to march proudly through the streets as adoring multitudes praised us for our heroism and admired our puffed out chests. I was eight years old then, and since finding that Indian boy, I see killing with much different eyes. What honor can there be in the slaughter of your fellow man? What splendor can there be in dying on a battlefield? Do these men really desire to kill one another, or do they fancy an eight year old's wish for glory?

I do not know how it came about that Southern states allow slavery while states in the North do not. I am not in favor of slavery, and I do not like the way some slaves are treated, but it seems to me that there should be a means besides warfare to settle our differences.

Mr. Lincoln wants to quickly put down this rebellion and save the Union. I can tell by the determination of those men hurrying to join the Confederacy that ending this rebellion will not be quick and easy. While men from the North seem to want that glory that I now find childish, men from the South are angry and wish to protect their homeland even if they have to die to do so.

Mr. Hatch sees a great war coming. I sincerely hope that he is wrong.

Sunday, May 19, 1861 day 49

It seems that we pass a grave every few miles. Some are freshly dug with crude crosses or wagon boards for markers. Some are old and grown over with weeds and only outlines bordered with rocks show that someone is buried beneath. Some are just nameless mounds waiting for time to make them indistinguishable from the rest of this treeless plain. Few have markers other than charcoal-scratched boards or painted stones containing the names and ages of the deceased. No marker seems permanent. Today we passed by a broken down and abandoned wagon. Much of the wagon had been stripped for the wheels and hardware, but someone had removed a board and painted with charcoal an epitaph to create a marker for a nearby unmarked grave; on it he dishonored the author of Jake's Smith & Oakes guide book:

**Here Lies the Body
of D.C. Oakes
Killed for Starting
This Gold Rush Hoax**

As we pass all these graves, it becomes evident that this is a dangerous journey and that disease, accidents, Indians or even rattle-snakes could cause any of us to soon be in permanent rest under one of these anonymous mounds of earth. I wish at this time to write a combination obituary, eulogy, and will to be read should I die at whatever service my companions choose for me, to whomever wishes to listen.

"Here we lay to rest Thomas Boone. Born on a Missouri farm, he learned the values of family, hard work and the love of God and man. He left for Colorado in 1861 at age sixteen to find gold and adventure. He never smoked, drank or bedded with a woman but held no grudges against those who did. He read whatever books he could borrow and was on his third reading of the Bible at the time of his departure. He believed in an afterlife and that all men and women, including Indians, coloreds and foreigners are created equal and will be with him in that place we call Heaven. He leaves behind precious few possessions and wishes for them to be divided equally among his surviving companions: To Whomever returns to Missouri first, yours is the burro train. Use it to travel through Grass Creek to return the Bible to his parents, the new moccasins to his brother Michael, and Holly to Becky Thompson. He leaves no regrets other than that he would have appreciated a longer life on this world."

In Eve's pack saddle, you will find ample ink to write this on a large stone:

Thomas Boone
1845-1861
Off on another adventure

Monday, May 20, 1861 day 50

It is certainly past midnight and I should have been asleep hours ago but I cannot close my eyes. I have my scatter gun at my side waiting for trouble. Jake is awake as well, resting against the wheel of the Watts' wagon with his Hawken on his lap. We had trouble today and Jake and I handled ourselves well. We both are now fearful of an ambush by two Southern slave traders. As there are ten in our group, I do not think that they will try anything... but they might, and I will not sleep until they are a few days behind us.

It all happened at about noon today while we were walking westward as we do each day. Jake and I were at the head of our group, Jake walking with Muffin, and I walking with the pack train. The four Germans, two Irishmen, and Isaiah Watts were close behind, each walking beside his pack horse or ox cart. Kaiden Watts was at the rear hauling the ox-drawn steam engine.

With the exception of a few scraggly bushes by the dry river bed to the left, there were no trees or large hills for miles to obstruct our view. For an hour, we had been gaining on a slow moving group of four, and by mid-morning they were about a half mile ahead of us.

"Look closely at that that group," Jake said.

I asked Isaiah for his spyglass. Travelers are certainly not out of the ordinary, but I could see that the four dots in the distance were going to change our day. Two men were on horseback and two black people were pulling a handcart. One of the black people appeared to be an old woman and the other walked with a heavy limp. "It's Mason and Martha!" I exclaimed. "It has to be!"

Our caravan came to a halt as we took turns looking to the forms slowly moving west. Through the spyglass we could see that it indeed was Mason and that he was pulling a loaded handcart while Martha helped by pushing it. The pulling of the cart appeared to be a great struggle for this lame boy and old woman. A rope was tied around Mason's neck with the other end tied to the saddle of a horse being ridden by one of the two horsemen. Each man was dressed in the manner of a person from one of the southern states, a butternut colored coat and a broad straw hat.

"We need to do something," I uttered, and everyone agreed for it was obvious that these two men had taken Mason and Martha hostage and were on their way, perhaps to Santa Fe, to sell them as slaves. When in Saint Louis, Jake's father had gone to a lawyer and had had proper freedom papers made for the two to prove that they were not escaped slaves. These two men likely had destroyed those papers.

Normally Jake lets others do the thinking and most of the heavy work, but he surprised me with, "I have a plan," as he grabbed his Smith and Oakes guide book out of a pannier on Muffin.

He carefully cut the inside cover out with his knife and said "Tom, I need ink and a blank piece of paper out of your journal." I protested at first that I need all my paper for writing but the impatient look on his face convinced me otherwise. "Paddy, I need a whiskey bottle!"

"Full or empty?" Paddy asked and again that look was displayed, so Paddy brought him a full one.

Jake inked the bottom of the bottle with some of my expensive blue ink and pressed it against the middle of a blank sheet of paper.

"Fill the top of this page with official looking writing," he demanded.

"What shall I write?" I asked.

"I don't care," he replied, "just make it look important."

I began writing a passage from the book of Psalms: *The lord is my Shepard I shall not want....* I forgot some of the next few lines but remembered *"Yea though I walk through the valley of the shadow of death, I will fear no evil,"* and by this time I was plenty afraid. Jake used the edge of the book and drew some lines on the bottom of the page under the blue stamped circle. He signed his name inside the blue circle and asked me to sign my name on one of the three lines. Paddy and Isaiah each signed one of the other two lines. Then Jake folded the two pieces of paper so that the book's inner cover with its bold printed title showed on the outside and the written page with the blue circle was on the inside. He then wrinkled the paper a bit, rubbed some dirt on the folds and stuffed what looked like an official document into his shirt pocket.

All of us were asking Jake what the plan was, but he told us to just remain silent and keep our guns at the ready. We set our caravan again in motion and overcame Mason, Auntie Martha and the two horsemen in about a half hour.

They moved to the side of the trail to allow us to pass as we approached. Auntie Martha and Mason did not even know it was us as we neared for they kept their heads bowed in the manner of slaves and looked only forward.

"What are you doing with my slaves!" Jake yelled at the top of his voice as we overtook the group.

"These Blackies are ours!" one of the butternut coated men yelled back. "We bought them from a wagon train fifty miles back and we have the bill of sale!"

"Your papers are worthless," Jake replied, still yelling, "This is Kansas. You cannot buy and sell slaves here."

Holly could sense the tension and started growling at the two strangers.

In a quieter voice Jake then said, "I have their legal paperwork right here in my hand." He then showed the two pages and proceeded to pretend to read the content of the papers. "It says right here on this document dated August 1, 1859....'by proclamation of Thomas Boone, Governor of the State of Maryland ... the two slaves known as Martha Washington and her son Mason are hereby the property of Jacob Lewis....' That's me!.. It further describes Martha as a woman of fifty-seven years with gray hair and a branded 'M' on her right elbow. It says here that the boy Mason is lame and has a scar on his left knee. Here, you can examine this paperwork," and he handed the papers to the taller of the two men.

Auntie Martha and Mason were standing very still and looking down at the ground. Jake then demanded in a gruff voice. "Let's see that elbow and that knee."

Auntie Martha responded, "Yessa Massa Jake" and pulled up her sleeve to reveal an ugly burn scar in the shape of the letter "M" while Mason pulled down his trousers to reveal the scar.

The man with the papers threw them on the ground and shouted just as loudly as Jake had, "We cain't read, but we cain shoot." He grabbed his musket and was about to point it at Jake when he saw that ten rifles, muskets, or shotguns were pointed at his head.

"Very well," he calmly spoke as he untied Mason's rope. The two men hopped on their horses and quickly rode east, back in the direction opposite our destination. When they were out of rifle range, one of them turned in his saddle and yelled, "I wouldn't sleep if I were you."

Paddy Donohoo bellowed back in his raspy Irish brogue, "May the devil take your soul and the buzzards eat your bones!" and fired his musket in their direction.

Jake has proven himself to be cunning and brave, but he sits there by the wagon wide awake. All this action happened twelve hours ago. I have no desire to close my eyes, and I do not think that I shall sleep for days.

Tuesday, May 21, 1860 day 51

It is good to have Auntie Martha and Mason in our group. The two southern traders were in such a hurry to leave that they left much of their supplies in Mason's handcart. Auntie Martha's tin washtub and iron were in the handcart as well as oats, cornmeal, flour, and a keg of water. A heavy cast iron skillet belonging to one of the traders had been left behind as well as a bag of bacon. Auntie Martha fried us up bacon and made biscuits for supper tonight, our best meal since leaving Grizzly Hatch's trading post. Mason did not have to pull that handcart today. I made only minor adjustments and was able to harness it to Number 4. Mason and Auntie Martha walk beside Number 4 and the cart. They travel with much more difficulty than do those of us with young healthy legs, but neither complains or slows the progress of our caravan.

Near sunset we happened upon some water in a gully left by a quick afternoon thunderstorm. Though there was no shelter here, we stopped for the evening and watered our animals in the murky water. Auntie Martha insisted that we remove our "smelly attire" tonight so that she might clean them. Mason built a small fire beneath the tub and Martha washed, rinsed, and then pressed all our clothing with a hot iron heated on the coals of the fire. It took her a full three hours to launder it all, and she managed to cook that bacon while our clothing dried on trees in the breeze. We were a little reluctant to sit with only blankets wrapped around us, but Auntie Martha kept her eyes diverted. Mason spent the entire three hours assisting her by tending the fire and performing any task she desired.

Mason still had his mouth organ and played it in the company of Sean Donohoo's fiddle, my Ozark jaw harp and Jake's mouth organ. Auntie Martha is a good singer, and for the first time since we left Grass Creek, I heard a female voice singing. Auntie Martha and Mason are a most welcome addition to our traveling party, and not one of us cares what color their skin is. Only Number 4 seems to object to the newcomers as she now has to pull that cart.

Friday, May 24, 1861 day 54

In the distance to the west we can see a white triangle jutting from the plains. Surely this speck of white is Pike's Peak and we are much closer than Mr. Hatch indicates. We can be no farther than a day's walk away and we are eager for the morning to arrive. I shall write no more tonight, as we have plans to discuss for tomorrow's end to this tedious trek.

CHAPTER 6
Buckskin Joe

Old Tom

We did not reach Pike's Peak the next day or the day after it for that matter, for it took four more days to reach the base of that mountain. We nearly ran out of water and would have surely died had it not been for the whiskey barrels we had worked so hard for. We soon found that Pike's Peak, though truly magnificent and enormous, was just a landmark for books such as Jake's guide and that the gold fields were another eighty to over a hundred miles away depending upon which route we took. Only Jake and I chose to head directly into the mountains, a more difficult but shorter route. The Watts brothers and their German friends, as well as the Donohoo brothers, all chose to head for the Denver area, where they could "mine the miners."

The Watts' wished to find a wooded area in which to set up a timber operation. The Germans were just interested in seeking employment. I always suspected that the Donohoos headed north with them as they had observed a wagonload of whiskey headed in that direction. Auntie Martha and Mason chose to go to Denver, as well. They had traveled over a thousand miles now with that tin wash tub and heavy iron and had but fifty or sixty miles to go to realize their dreams of real freedom from slavery. I was sad to see them go.

By this time, we had heard of the conflict beginning between the northern and southern states. It had now been a month since Fort Sumter, in South Carolina, had been fired upon, and both sides were now preparing for war. Four more states: Virginia, Arkansas, Tennessee and North Carolina had joined the Confederacy. Missouri had chosen to stay with the Union for the time being, as a slave state, but factions within the state were fighting each other.

Monday, May 27, 1861 day 57

We are finally within sight of the Platte River and the mountains bearing the gold. We found a trading post at the base of Pike's Peak where for two bits Jake bought a map of the shortcut to the gold fields. There are two ways to get there. Those with wagons must first travel seventy miles north to Denver City and then follow the South Platte River for about fifty miles. They must then cross a mountain pass and travel a twenty mile path to the gold fields. Those without wagons and willing to climb, may cut straight west along an old Indian path through the mountains and intersect the Platte River in about fifty miles. Then an easy journey of thirty or forty miles will get you there.

All of our friends headed toward Denver City to find their fortunes. At Jake's insistence, he and I chose to climb mountains. We did find the path and found the map to be fairly accurate, but were not warned how treacherous climbing straight uphill at times could be. Muffin strained with the walk as did other horses we encountered.

Occasionally we met someone foolish enough to attempt a mountain crossing with wagons, oxen, or both. Those people had to turn back. My animals had an easy time climbing with their loads. I would lead with Eve and the others would follow in her footsteps. Eve steps forward with a front hoof and then the other as if to test the rocky path for solid ground. She then puts her rear hooves in the exact spots of her front hoof prints leaving only two prints in the dusty path. The others in turn place their hoofs in those same prints left by Eve and none of them ever stumble on the side of the rocky path. Muffin, Jake, and I are the only ones to slip or trip, and we did it with great frequency.

It has taken us a full week to travel fifty miles, most of it uphill. Tonight we are on the top of what they call a mountain pass and are now looking over a vast grassy plain. This plain is rimmed by tall snow covered mountains. These mountains, they say, are the gold-bearing mountains and somewhere beneath that snow is the gold that will make us rich. In the near distance to the west we see the river. We will walk down to that river tomorrow and then follow it to those bluish peaks in the west. They beckon us as if saying, "Come and harvest our riches." After nearly two months of traveling I still cannot judge distances, but I think we will be in those mountains in two days.

Tuesday, May 28, 1861 day 58

Walking downhill is as difficult as walking uphill. While less exhausting, it is easier to lose my footing and is much more dangerous. Again the burros, as I now call them, have shown themselves to be sure-footed. Our aim today was to reach the far off river at a place where we could see that the grass was taller and greener than any grass we had seen since Missouri. We were sure we would find a spring at this place and we could rest and water the animals for a couple of hours.

When we approached that destination, two Indian women ran out of the lush grass. I do not know whether they were washing clothing or bathing, but they fled their hiding place in the grass when they determined that we were heading for that very spot. They had no horses to ride and ran for nearly a mile before they came to the safety of a hill and a few trees. This was the first close up encounter with Indians in our entire journey, though we have no doubt that Indians have watched our every move. Tonight we will not light fires, and we will stay on guard all night long.

As we approached this nearly treeless river we observed that the river was steaming near that place where the grass grew tall and deep green. Neither Jake nor I had ever seen water steam other than from a hot kettle so we walked to that spot and put our hands in the water. It was warm. The animals refused to drink the water, perhaps because of the smell of boiling eggs or perhaps because they preferred cool water so we led them upstream a few yards. The grass was tall and lush and we allowed them to graze and rest for a full two hours. Jake and I could not resist the warm water, and while one of us kept guard against Indians, the other bathed. As there are no trees or hills for a mile we had plenty warning if an Indian or traveler was approaching. None came. I soaked in the warm water for over an hour and tonight I feel clean and refreshed.

As I write this tonight I think about Mr. Hatch's tale of mud boiling out of the ground and wonder if it might be true after all. I now wonder if there really are bears as big as draft horses with teeth as sharp as razors or Indian women who wear no clothes. It is now time to quit writing and take my turn watching for Indians. Tonight I am a bit more nervous than usual.

Thursday, May 30, 1861 day 60

Two months since we left Grass Creek, we finally reached the gold camps at about noon. We arrived here by the shorter way of cutting northwest straight through the mountains from Pike's Peak and scarcely saw a soul for an entire week. Now we are where the South Platte River meets the tall mountains and there are men everywhere.

Certainly hundreds and perhaps thousands of men are digging into the bank of this river and every stream emptying into it for miles around. Jake and I found a spot with no miner panning for the gold in it and proceeded to dig into the rocky bank for its riches. We had only begun to shovel into the rocky bank when we saw a bearded man walking toward us with a shotgun pointed at us.

"Put the shovels away and scram, you filthy claim jumpers!" was all he said, and we apologized and hurried into the booming little city of Fair Play Diggings. We found a tent that sold hot cider for two bits a mug and treated ourselves to an expensive toast to the end of our journey. Tonight we will ask around this bustling little city to see if anyone will tell us how and where to look for gold and what it means to "stake a claim."

Saturday, June 15, 1861 day 76

We have been in the mountains for two weeks now. Jake and I have not found one bit of gold, and we are nearly out of food. It is apparent that we will not strike it rich soon, for it seems that we do not know how to do so or even where to look. Whenever we find a stream that seems promising, we also find someone with a musket pointed at our heads demanding that we "claim jumpers" move along and forfeit what few gold colored specks we have found. We do not know if these tiny yellow stones that we find are even gold. Everywhere there is the talk about the strike up north of here near the town of Buckskin Joe. This camp is at the top of the world. "Just follow the Platte River 'til it narrows enough for the trees on opposite banks to touch, then follow Buckskin Gulch 'til it meets the sky." Tomorrow we shall load up what little supplies we have left and seek employment in this new town.

June 1, 1861

Dear Mother and Father,

I am finally high in the mountains in gold country.

Jake and I made it here in just over eight weeks, very much alive and well. The gold does not glisten in the river-beds waiting to be scooped up as I had hoped, but I believe that fortune can still be found with a little hard work. We have not learned yet how to successfully find these riches but are becoming more educated each day. I still plan to return this fall as soon as I discover this treasure which I now know is buried somewhere near here.

I trust that the crops were all successfully planted and are growing well in the warm June sunshine. I have seen plenty of mules on this adventure but none are as fine as the ones we breed. I miss you both as well as Michael. I miss Mother's fine cooking, my soft bed in the loft, a roof to hide under when the weather turns, and Grass Creek in general, but I am in good health and happy to be here.

The mountains here are magnificent and very much larger than the hills of Missouri, though not as green as I would have thought. Unlike horses, the donkeys seem to be not bothered at all about climbing or descending steep rocky paths and I am glad to have them with me, though I still long for a horse to ride.

I will write again soon when I find more permanent lodging. Please give my regards to Michael and to Becky Thompson if you happen to see her. If you wish to write to me, you may mail a letter to me in care of The Fair Play Diggings, Colorado Territory.

Affectionately your son,
Tom

Monday, June 17, 1861 day 78

This may be journey's end, and I will have no further need to count the days away from home. We followed the South Platte River for six miles from the settlement called Fair Play Diggings to a little creek and then followed a very rough wagon road beside that creek. The road seemed almost straight up, making us wonder how wagons could traverse such a treacherous trail. Once, numerous trees grew here, but most have been recently cut down for logs and firewood. Even without the trees, this is the most beautiful place I have seen on this journey and perhaps the most beautiful spot on earth. Completely surrounding us are majestic mountains with snow covered peaks. These mountains are rumored to be even taller than Pike's Peak, but no one knows for sure how tall any mountain is. Buckskin Creek trickles by the path with a sound that I find very comforting. The sky is of a deep blue color that I didn't know existed in the natural world, not even in flowers, a blue with no hint of the gray that seems always present in Missouri. Though totally different from any landscape I have ever seen or even known to exist, I feel at home here!

I keep my pack train in the same order as the day I started. Eve, walks with me, followed by Adam, Number 3, Number 4, Cain, and Abel. I decided long ago that Number 3 and Number 4 are good names for the two middle burros and it frequently brings smiles when someone inquires of their names. Holly trots behind, barking at the heels of Cain and Abel to keep them moving.

At times on the trip across the plains there were twelve to sixteen companions traveling in a pack for safety, but all that remains with me is Jake Lewis, who started out of Grass Creek with me back in April. This faithful friend who was once so eager to travel fast and carelessly has now walked without complaining for the past five hundred miles. We have become better friends than we ever were as children.

Though it is the middle of June and certainly scorching hot back in Missouri, I could see our breath as we walked into the town of

Buckskin Joe this morning. There are about twenty buildings in the town, mostly unpainted stores or saloons crudely erected of logs or rough hewn lumber and about a hundred dwellings for which the word "house" would be an exaggeration. Most of these structures are not much more than tents for they consist of a square of logs stacked on top of each other up to a height of two to four feet and then a tent of canvas or just plain branches and dirt over these logs. Guessing from the freshly cut color of the logs and lumber, I think that there is not a building in town more than a few months old and many new structures are going up as I write. Snow is still resting in shoveled heaps on shaded sides of most buildings. Judging from the number of camp sites near the town, I guess the population to be near a thousand men, and only men. I have not seen a woman, other than Auntie Martha and a couple of running Indians, since the wagon load of evening doves passed us weeks ago.

Near the center of this hastily constructed town are two loaded freight wagons with a sign leaning against a wheel proclaiming:

H. A. W. TABOR
GENERAL MERCHANDISE AND GRUBSTAKING

The wagons are loaded with sacks of flour, grain and smoked meats as well as picks, shovels, pans and buckets. How these wagons got up that treacherous path seems a miracle. Nearby four men were busy with shovels digging a rectangular base for what I imagine to be a more permanent store than two uncovered wagons.

One of the diggers yelled "nice burro train!"

With pride, I yelled back "Thank you." Then, in reference to the sign, I yelled "What's grubstaking?"

A man about thirty years old with a heavy mustache walked towards us and spoke as if reciting a memorized poem, "My name is Horace Tabor. If you boys are in need of food and supplies, I can equip you with tools, meals and all necessary provisions, as needed, in order for you to find all the gold and riches to be found. The food is free, tools can be paid for with the gold you find, and all I ask is thirty percent of your profits in return for my generosity."

"No thank you Mr. Tabor," I told him, "what we really need now are jobs."

"If you are lacking money," he continued, "I will buy whatever grain you have in those bags."

I replied that my corn meal, oats, and flour were not for sale, and he then offered me a dollar a bag, or about ten times what they were worth in Grass Creek. "They are still not for sale Mr. Tabor… What would I eat?"

"Why son, you may eat whatever Mrs. Tabor cooks for all my hands. You boys do seek work, do you not?"

To Jake, he offered a job of three bits a day, plus grub, for ten hours of hard work building his store. Jake, nearly out of money and almost totally out of food, agreed immediately. To me he said. "Kid, with those burros you don't need employment, you need a partner. A horse is not much good around here for hauling loads, but this pack train will suit me fine."

"What do you propose?" I asked.

"Why, we can load this train with merchandise, and you may help me peddle goods to the miners up at the diggings."

"Up?" I didn't know it could get any higher than this, but his offer of a dollar a day, plus ten percent of sales, plus food seemed most generous and I agreed. "This bag of corn meal is for sale," I said and sold him one of my two remaining bags.

He wished to pay me in four tin tokens worth a quarter dollar each at his store, but I didn't trust him or his tokens. I accepted only a gold dollar piece which he reluctantly gave me. His tokens are octagonal pieces of cut tin about the size of a silver dollar and stamped with a large letter "T" on one side and a value such as 5¢ directly under the "T." They may be redeemed for merchandise at his store.

He gave us the rest of the day to set up camp with orders to show up for breakfast one half hour after sunrise.

Jake and I set up a campsite near the Tabor Store. We had to walk more than a half mile to find trees to fell for logs, and we dragged eight of them to town, one at a time, behind my burro train. They did not like the work but cooperated with a little persuasion from Holly. We arranged the logs into a square and piled them two logs deep to make the base of our little "house." We chinked the logs with leaves and dirt to keep the wind from blowing through. On top of these logs we erected our canvas much like a tent. In front of our place we built a fire which keeps us somewhat warm for the nights here are downright cold for June.

Tomorrow I begin working and earning money, and I am very thankful. As I sit here and write under the canvas and in front of this warm fire, I think with amusement at what my job will be. Who would have ever thought that donkeys could be a source of employment?

Old Tom

I now was beginning to realize that my father was wiser than I had given him credit for. Mark Twain once said, "When I was a boy of fourteen, my father was so ignorant I could hardly stand to have the old man around. But when I got to be twenty-one, I was astonished at how much the old man had learned in seven years."

Father may not have been willing to give me the mule that I so desperately wanted but he perhaps knew that donkeys were being used in Mexico and California as beasts of burden in and around mines.

I had now traveled perhaps a thousand miles with my pack ani-
mals and had come to respect their worthiness. A mere four months
ago I was angry that my father would not let loose of even one of his
precious mules or horses and I was forced to travel West in shame
with six worthless asses. In the mountains I learned that with their
sure footedness they could go where a horse could not, and now I was
finding that with their help I could command a better wage than Jake
who was a full head taller than me and much stronger.

Monday, June 24, 1861

I have been working for a week now and feel almost no disappointment in not finding gold for I am now earning more than two
dollars a day. Jake and I arrive for breakfast at daybreak to find Mrs.
Tabor already busy cooking flapjacks on a huge griddle over a bed
of coals. Helping her is a freed black man who works silently at her
side. Each man who arrives at that hour gets as many flapjacks as he
can eat and two pieces of fried salt pork or venison. I have not eaten
this well since Auntie Martha cooked us breakfast a month ago.

Augusta Tabor is a remarkable woman. She must be the only
woman in this town, and she doesn't seem to notice or care as she is
tremendously devoted to Horace. I guess her to be nearly thirty years
old. She has round spectacles, tightly bundled brown hair and a sun-
weathered face, all of which make her appear to be about five years
older. Her baby boy, Macksey plays in a square pen near the cooking
area and she is able to tend to him and the cooking at the same time.
While Horace Tabor likes to think of the store as being his, it is Augusta
who makes all the business decisions and does most of the work.

After the twelve to twenty paying customers depart for various
jobs and Jake and two others remain to build the store, I help Mrs.
Tabor and the black man known only as "Snowball" cook about two
hundred more corn or wheat flapjacks and about five pounds of salt
pork or fresh elk. We wrap everything in oilcloth, wrap the oilcloth
in blankets and I tie these packages securely on Adam and Eve. Mr.

Tabor helps me load nails, gold pans, whiskey, and buckets on Number 3 and Number 4 and lumber onto Cain and Abel. I at first had trouble tying boards to these two until Mr. Tabor showed me that to allow the lumber to drag was the best way to carry these large items. I then trek up to the needy men high in the canyon.

Leading my pack train, I walk uphill to the source of Buckskin Gulch. Along the way I give food to his "grubstakers," but sell hardware, lumber, food and whiskey to anyone who pays the price. I get to keep a tenth of all sales. I do not like having to sell whiskey in these little green bottles, but whisky is my most popular trade item, and I frequently run out of stock before I reach the top of my route.

I walk a seven mile traverse to the top of the world by following the creek which is already quite small by now. Soon I find myself treading between two walls of enormous mountains and am completely shaded from the sun, but all along the stream are men digging into the mountainside for ore and carrying buckets, sacks or blankets of this dirt to the stream to be panned for the gold in it. As I travel, grubstakers come to me and trade small tin tokens with a stamped "T" for food or supplies. I provide each man with Mrs. Tabor's warm flapjacks and two pieces of salt pork which they eat at once with their fingers. For a midday meal each man receives a hunk of elk jerky and two corn biscuits. Miners near the top of the stream nearly always buy my lumber and nails from which to make sluice boxes, whatever they are. I reach the lake at the end of the creek by around noon and I pan for gold for a couple of hours though I do not know how to do so. Sometimes I find a few gold-colored specks which I hope are valuable. As I head back down the path, some miners load bags of ore onto my pack saddles. With Mr. Tabor's permission I charge them five cents a bag for the privilege of bringing this ore to the assayers in Buckskin Joe, and I do not have to share this money with him. The men pay in tokens or coins and then walk with me, as they do not trust me with their fortunes. Many of these men are the prospectors that Mr. Tabor grubstakes. They came here with almost no money or food and are either too proud or too greedy to work for wages. Instead, they allow Mr. Tabor to provide them with all necessary food and equipment for that thirty percent share. Some men live in crude shacks or tents near their claims, but most live in town and come back before dark. Many eat dinners at the Tabor place. Mrs. Tabor usually cooks a hearty stew of meat, potatoes, and carrots or salt pork and beans and serves us into our own tin cups. We eat outside on whatever rock we can find for a chair.

As we sit around eating, talk is frequently of a coming war for it seems that there is no way to avoid one. While nearly half of the men are from northern states, about a third arrived here from states which have seceded from the Union, and the rest are immigrants from other countries. Many men, especially those from the South, plan to go home to fight for their states if a war should develop. Most of the immigrants came to America to find a better life and do not wish to take part in this dispute. I have no desire to fight, either. No matter which side Missouri chooses to side with, I will not be going home to enlist in a state militia. I have no desire to kill someone. I do not wish to die soon. I do not want to be a soldier. Jake and a whole lot of others feel the same as I do about this approaching conflict.

Tuesday, June 25, 1861

This town, the creek, and the gulch they lie in are named after a rawhide-wearing mountain man, who called himself "Buckskin Joe." He first discovered gold here but soon sold his claim when the population of the area became more than he cared for. He said that he could not tolerate city life and if his find created a city he would just have to "mosey on."

Some would like this village to become a great metropolis. A man named Dodge, who will be the postmaster here once we get mail delivery, now wants to name the town "Laurette" after his wife Laura and his daughter Jeanette back in Illinois. He seems to have political influence and money and applied for postal service here under that name. Most people don't seem to care what name will be on the new post office and continue to refer to this little city as Buckskin Joe. I favor the name Buckskin Joe, as well, for it seems to reflect the wild nature of this raw, untamed town.

As I get to know the town and many of its inhabitants, I find just how different it is from Grass Creek. Most notable is the landscape for as Grass Creek is flat and green, Buckskin Joe sits in a narrow valley with high mountains on either side and is void of any vegetation due to the trampling received from a couple thousand boots. While there is but one saloon in Grass Creek that is a quiet place with few customers, there are ten rowdy taverns in Buckskin Joe. I have not been in one, but I hear that they are crude places with dirt floors, no glass windows, and rough pine planks for tables. Some have two small rooms behind the bar; one is for the owner to sleep in, and the other is for the prostitute who makes her living there by doing things other than sleeping. I have seen some of these women at Mr. Tabor's store, and much like that wagon load of soiled doves I saw on the prairie, these ladies of the evening are pretty much an unfortunate looking group of toothless and fat old women.

There is no church here, but I hear that a traveling minister rides in once a week to preach The Word to whoever will listen. I hear that "Father Dyer," as he is called, bellows out energetic sermons that we used to call back home "fire and brimstone," against the sins of this wild and untamed little city. I suspect most here are indifferent to his words, but I welcome the idea of any place of worship, even if I must stand in the street to participate. I shall attend his service this Sunday afternoon, and I will bring my Bible.

Wednesday, June 26, 1861

I am learning how to pan for gold. Instead of using one of my pots as many gold seekers do, I have hammered out a shallow pan about twelve inches round and three inches deep out of that piece of tin I got from Mrs. Hultgren. It is a simple makeshift affair and does not look much like a pan at all as I have left numerous hammer pocks in it, but I find that these imperfections sometimes trap

94

little flakes of gold. First I dig a few shovelfuls of dirt near the diamond-shaped lake I call Kite Lake for its nearly square appearance. I remove all rocks and debris, fill six canvas bags with this ore and carry them down to the water for panning. I fill the pan with ore and swirl it around under the water until all that is left is black sand and a few shiny gold colored flakes. I remove those flakes which are large enough to grasp with my fingers and put them in a small jar. Mostly the gold I find is smaller than a grain of salt and I cannot separate it from the black sand, but frequently I find nuggets the size of an alfalfa seed, and once I lucked upon a nugget almost the size of a pea. These little nuggets can be sold at the assayer's office for as much as a dollar.

Thursday, June 27, 1861

As I get to know the people in this town, I realize that I was wrong about there being no women. Many men travel with wives and sometimes even small children. Percival T. Coty, his wife Caroline, and their three children are one such family I have gotten to know and like. They all live in the assayer's office, which has become a vital part of this mining district. For a fee, Coty, as he likes to be called, will check your gold or gold ore and tell you its value. He will then buy it or give you an assessment of its worth. I do not know how he can tell you the purity of those little yellow flakes, but I do know that it involves fire, a liquid that I think might be an acid, and that little eyepiece he keeps in his pocket.

This seems a harsh place to raise children, but they all seem to be happy. Caroline has sent an order to Denver for some boiled linseed oil and a little iron oxide to put in it. She plans for the assayer's office to be the first building in Buckskin Joe to be painted. The iron oxide will make the oil turn red, and if more children arrive to Buckskin Joe, this red structure will serve as the town's school house where she will be the teacher.

Friday, June 28, 1861

Each day for the past ten days I have peddled whiskey to the miners; each day for the past ten days I have walked home past a half dozen saloons with men foolishly throwing their money down for a few shots of the vile spirits. I cannot help but wonder why men pay so much of their hard earned income for a drink that makes them act so foolishly.

I hear that Reverend Dyer preaches nearly every Sunday against the sin of alcohol and just as often hecklers in the skirts of his open air church mock his yelling and openly chug drinks out of their whiskey bottles as he preaches.

I do not know why the drinking of whiskey is a sin. I know that Noah got drunk and that God was displeased, but Jesus' first miracle was to turn water into wine. Perhaps the drinking of whiskey is a sin, but the drinking of wine is not. I would like to taste wine some day, but I do not have the courage to buy it.

Saturday, June 29, 1861

The Silver Slipper Saloon is the largest, finest and newest establishment in town and the only one large enough for one to move around in freely. Mostly, I hear, it has a dirt floor, but in the center of the room is a plank surface that Big Al, the German bartender, says will be for dancing. Until today I didn't understand why there would be a need for a dance floor, because the only women in town are a few ugly whores who do their dancing on their backs, a few wives who stay in their cabins with their husbands and children, and Mrs. Coty, and Mrs. Tabor.

Today Mrs. Tabor sent me to the Silver Slipper with two bags of lime to trade for two clay jugs of Kentucky bourbon. The lime will be used by Big Al to make whitewash for the saloon and the bourbon will be poured by Mrs. Tabor into little green bottles to be sold to the miners. I find these bottles on the ground as I travel, and Mrs. Tabor gives me a penny for each one that I return to her.

As I was unloading the bags from Adam, a wagon arrived with kegs of beer, barrels of whiskey, and other supplies for the saloon. Sitting on the buckboard with the driver was the most beautiful woman I have ever seen. She was perhaps twenty-four or twenty-five years old with a flawless complexion, almost coal black hair, large blue eyes and a constant smile. I walked to the buckboard when it stopped and held out my hand to help her down. First she tipped her bonnet and then gently reached for my shaking hand. She sprang lightly from the wagon with ease and I was awed by her grace. "My name's Tom... Thomas Boone," I stuttered.

"Good to meet you, Tom... Thomas Boone," she said but didn't offer her name, and just asked if I could help her with her carpet bag. Gladly I carried it into the saloon for her and went back to get the two bags of lime. I had no more than placed the two heavy cloth sacks on the floor when Big Al handed me the two jugs of bourbon and said. "Begone Kid, Miss Silverheels and I have business to discuss."

Many around here aren't known by their Christian names but by nicknames. The few negroes who live here remain hidden in the woods and are known only by names such as "Snowball," Black Bob," or "Digger." In addition to Buckskin Joe, and Big Al, we have Smilen George, Little Bill, Hard-a-Hearin Harry, Gold Dust, Rocken Rob, and Mountain George. Because of my meager sixteen years of age and my youthful looks, most men call me "Kid." I guess Miss Silverheels is as good a name as any. If I ever see her again, I hope that she remembers that my name is Tom as "Kid" is an embarrassment and I do not like that name.

Sunday, June 30, 1861

Today is Sunday and I went to the first church service conducted by a real minister since I left Grass Creek more than three months

ago. Though it is almost July, today was rather cold and windy. Word
had been passed that a Reverend John Dyer would arrive at noon
and preach to us in the street, as there is no church building here,
nor is there even a structure large enough to hold more than twenty
men. There were about thirty men and one woman standing and waiting when a tall muscular man of about fifty years, carrying a heavy
Bible and a well worn hymnal, arrived on horseback. He had barely
dismounted when he began bellowing about our sinful ways. He
shouted that we were on the path to Hell, that we should burn all the
saloons and other places of ill character, and that we needed to share
no less than ten percent of our wealth with the Lord. With no church
to build or maintain, I wondered what the Lord needed with ten percent of the earnings of thirty men. I also prefer to hear readings from
the Bible to a scolding, and he rambled on for over an hour, so my
mind wandered. It did not have far to wander for that one woman in
our midst was Miss Silverheels. She is a beauty to look at, even when
her hair is bundled under a bonnet and she is wearing a woolen coat.
When we sang "Rock of Ages," I could hear her voice above all others. It sounded as glorious as the song of a meadow lark, yet comical,
for it seemed that this bird was singing her songs of praise along with
a choir of grunting pigs. Reverend Dyer took off his thick woolen hat
to expose the only head of gray hair I had seen in months, and passed
it around for a collection. Jake whispered to me that they must call
him "Father" Dyer because he was old enough to be the father or
even grandfather of anyone in town. I would have been more gener-

98

ous had I been sitting in a warm pew rather than standing on a breezy street, so a flake of gold about the size of a pepper seed was all I dropped in that old gray hat. Father Dyer thanked us, put the offerings in a canvas sack, and rode out of town to the next mining camp where he would surely find even more sinners and another offering. I shall attend the service again each Sunday from now on, but I sorely long for Reverend Johnson's quiet readings, the pianoforte, and the clean white church back in Grass Creek.

Thursday, July 4, 1861

Today is Independence Day, and though I had to make my run, I didn't pan for gold and came back to town early. Many men took the day off to celebrate, not perhaps so much out of patriotism as for a good excuse to get drunk. Few men seemed to be working their claims, and all day long I could hear the sounds of guns being shot into the air. At sundown the Silver Slipper held a celebration. A fiddle player was playing music and Miss Silverheels performed a couple of dances outside on top of an empty flat bed wagon. Wearing a scarlet dress with white lace, she flitted and twirled around with delicate grace to the music. As she twirled, we all could see her very shapely legs all the way from those dainty silver slippers to well above her knees. She is by far the most beholding creature I have ever laid my eyes upon. There must have been two hundred of us standing and watching this performance, all straining to see as much as possible. I had never seen anything like this before and stood there silently. When it got dark, she and the fiddle player went inside the Silver Slipper and many men followed. For ten cents, the men could dance with her on that wooden platform, while the fiddler played a song, and the line for that opportunity went outside the door. A prospector named Scotty Browne told me that for two dollars, she would dance without that scarlet dress on, and for a hundred dollars she might dance in bed with you, and starting today, he was going to save as much money as he could. I quickly replied, "I don't believe you. No lady that flawless would find money more valuable than her chastity and good name." Besides, a whore will sell her fare for two bits to a dollar, so why would a man part with the fortune of half a year's income to lay with Miss Silverheels, anyway?

Friday, July 5, 1861

Today Jake didn't help build The Tabor Store. Instead he was instructed to ride Muffin to the Fair Play Diggings to buy an ox. Mr. Tabor gave Jake twenty-five dollars to find the fattest animal he could get. Jake rode out this morning and if I had a horse, I would have joined him just for the sport of it. Most things here cost about ten times what they do back home, but oxen here are worn out from the trip and cost no more than their value back east. He found no such animal with any weight but came back with a skinny cow that he bought for just twenty dollars from a newly arrived miner desperate for money. Mr. Tabor was pleased and immediately put the ox on a diet of grain and plenty of fresh water. A crowd of men cheered when they saw Jake arrive pulling that unfortunate animal with a rope for it means good cuts of fresh meat will soon be available for sale. Mrs. Tabor will use the lesser cuts of beef to make those delicious stews. With the remaining five dollars, Jake was able to buy a sack of onions and a sack of carrots. My mother would throw away vegetables in such a sad condition as those in the sacks, but Augusta will work her magic on them, and the stew will be delicious. She sometimes walks into a sunny meadow and finds greens to add to her stews, but mostly the only vegetables we get are those withered onions and carrots.

I have to admit that I miss the vegetables that come out of Mother's garden at this time of year. We would have been eating fresh peas, radishes and strawberries for over a month by now; and green beans, tomatoes, and squash would soon be on the table. There are no fresh fruits or vegetables here in the mountains, and I wonder if it is even possible to grow a garden in this cool weather. Fresh raspberries and cream on one of Mother's warm shortcakes would now taste like a treat from heaven.

July 6, 1861

My dearest Becky,

I am alive and well and living at the top of the world in this place we now call Colorado. Jake and I arrived to the mountains in about six weeks and found our way to a town called Buckskin Joe last week. I found no gold, but I make good money carrying supplies up to the miners on my pack train. I sell them food and supplies from a small general store. Who would have thought that a donkey would be so valuable here? We call them burros, and they can easily carry a load to where no horse would or could venture.

Holly is doing well and walks with me each day on my route. Her chest is now the height of my knees, and her coat has developed into the dark brown color of a fine cup of chocolate. She is a great companion and is rarely out of my sight.

Soon there will be a postal service here in Buckskin Joe, but politicians are bickering over its name. I think that the name will be Laurette after some loudmouth's wife and daughter, so if you wish to write me try addressing it to that place.

I think of you often and wish you lived just down the road as before. Had I known how sorely I would miss you, I might never have made this quest. I miss those walks home from church on Sundays. I wish you were here to see how beautiful this place is. I miss your cookies.

I still plan to come home wealthy and start that store, but I now see that I will not have enough money to do so until at least next spring. Will you be there?

Warmly,

Thomas Boone

CHAPTER 7
Wolves and Sheep

Saturday, July 6, 1861

I once thought that everyone who came here would be looking for gold, but many seem to come here for business opportunity. Today a most unlikely small wagon entered town. It was pulled by an average-size brown riding pony and had only the driver and one passenger. The contents of this canvas-covered wagon were just a meager amount of food, supplies, and a small old printing press. The driver, whose name was Mike Armstrong, was a wiry and nearly toothless man about twenty-two years old who came here to find gold. He got free passage for driving the wagon and providing protection with his shotgun. The owner of the wagon and printing press was an unlikely-looking fellow to have traveled all the way from Baltimore, for while he was of average height, he was also somewhat chubby with a pasty complexion. He is older than many miners, perhaps forty years old, wears a black tailored suit, round spectacles, and a tall black beaver hat, making him look more like an eastern tycoon than a rough and hardy prospector. Richard Hamilton is his name and he has traveled two thousand miles to start a printing business and weekly newspaper. As I have never seen one before, I am fascinated by the old printing press and offered to help the two men set up camp or find lodging.

Mike, whose obligations are now ended, walked to one of the boarding houses where for twenty-five cents a night, he can sleep in a large tent with perhaps a dozen other men. For his two bits a day he most likely will share a straw stuffed mattress with one or two other miners and receive a breakfast of biscuits and coffee and a dinner of beans or stew.

By raising the canvas onto curved poles and moving his printing press to an adjoining tent, Richard and I made a tiny dwelling out of his small wagon. In addition to the old printing press, he also has a small iron stove. I have seen stoves before but never one this tiny, for it is only about waist high and cannot hold a very large piece of wood.

I was so captivated by that old press that I spent much of the day helping Richard set up business in that canvas tent. The press is about fifty years old, made mostly of wood and iron, and weighs as much as two grown men. A heavy iron plate is supported between two sturdy oak uprights as tall as my eyes and moves up and down between those uprights by means of a lever. I helped him set the type for Buckskin Joe's first printed advertisement. We placed big wooden letters and smaller lead letters, one at a time in a flat box he calls the "bed," inked the letters with a leather dauber, and placed a sheet of paper over that inked bed. Richard then placed the whole thing under the iron press and pulled the lever. This caused the ink to be pressed onto the paper which Richard hung over a line to dry. When the ink dried, we pasted the copy to a board and set the newly created sign on the ground outside his tent. It reads:

THE BUCKSKIN PRESS

WEEKLY NEWS OF THE AREA AND THE WORLD

Also handbills, cards and legal printing

I asked how he would receive weekly news of the world in this remote location and Mr. Hamilton just smiled.

When I told Richard of my fondness for writing, he suggested that I write a paragraph a week for the paper. I agreed immediately though I do not know what I should like to write about. It certainly will not be news for I know little of what is happening outside of Buckskin Joe.

Monday, July 8, 1861

The mountains here are truly massive creations of wonder. I am in awe that God could create such beauty in such an otherwise cold and barren place. There are many names for each mountain, but none are official. Most of the peaks have ten or twelve names usually describing its shape. Horseshoe Mountain is the only one most agree on because of its inverted "U" shape seemingly scoured off a side of it. My favorite peak is one to the northeast about ten miles away. It stands alone from the others and rises elegantly, like a princess above the Fair Play Diggings. Others call it Cone Mountain, White Mountain, Mount Carson, after the explorer, Mount Jefferson, for the president, Dead Widow Peak, Saw Tooth and a dozen other names. This mountain is surely a woman, and I call it Goddess Peak for her grace and beauty. Someday, I shall climb that goddess, erect a flag, and claim her as mine.

Tuesday, July 9, 1861

I am a thousand miles from home, and sometimes I feel less safe than when we were on the trail. I sometimes feel that I live amongst wolves. There is no law here, only the law of the pack. If you run with the pack, then you will not be eaten. I came to this realization when I stopped today at one of my regular stops, the "Wolves' Den." It is a saloon run by a very large man known as "Little Bill." Little Bill promotes himself by wearing a wolf's head as a hat in mountain man fashion, making him seem almost seven feet tall. His saloon is the most dreadful establishment in town with log walls and a canvas roof. As there are no windows, the only light comes through unchinked cracks in the logs and the canvas roof. At night it is lit by only one or two oil lamps. The saloon is small, about the size of a chicken coop with barely enough headroom to stand up, and inside this dark place is an eight foot long plank bar, a table with four chairs, and little else. The rough wood plank rests on two barrels and men stand in front of it drinking while Little Bill fills their glasses with cheap whiskey. At the solitary table sits Lancelot Slade playing cards. He is a wolf. He is one of the many who came to the gold fields not to find gold by hard work, but to prey on those who came here to toil. There are many such men here, and a few women, who I think of as wolves. Little Bill with his watered down whiskey is a wolf, so is Horace Tabor with his high priced food and practice of grubstaking starving prospectors. Bar Keep Miller, and all the whores, are wolves. They came here with no hopes of finding gold other than that which they can wrest free from the honest worker, or "sheep," as I have come to think of the honest worker. Everyone travels here with some money, and most who work hard find gold here even if it is a dollar's worth a day or less. It is the job of these wolves to remove this gold from the careless, the foolish, or the lonely. At the same time it is these wolves who enforce, not the laws of the land, but the laws of the pack. The laws of the pack are simple:

1. Thou shall not jump a claim.
2. Thou shall not steal a horse or cheat at cards.
3. You may not kill a man without good cause.
4. Honor the self-proclaimed leaders of the pack.

Everything else is legal unless you wrong a good standing member of the pack. There is a pine tree near the mouth of Mosquito gulch which everyone calls "The Hanging Tree." It has more than one grave mound beside it for those who have disobeyed the law of the pack.

I do not earn my living by digging for gold, but instead I ease the work of the prospectors by carrying loads on my burros that a horse or man could not. I do not consider myself to be a wolf, but maybe I am. The goods that I sell certainly make Mr. Tabor huge profits of which I get a ten percent share. I do not consider Miss Silverheels, or Jake, or anyone else who works for a living to be a wolf either, but our boots do not get cold and wet in the creek. We tend to the needs of the sheep as well as the wolves, and are left alone so long as we follow their laws.

Lancelot Slade seems evil. He is only of average height but his shoulders are wide and his arms look like they belong on a bear. His teeth have a greenish cast when you can see them past his unlit cigar. His eyes are squinty as if he is trying hard to see right through you. His face is scarred and that head is permanently cocked to one side indicating that Mr. Slade has been in numerous brawls. He came here for no other purpose than to win at cards and he makes a lot of money doing so. His scheme seems to be to make the rest of the men at the table so nervous that they make errors or fold with a good hand because of that fierce stare. He keeps a knife on the table as if he wishes to catch you cheating and is rumored to have cut the fingers off a player he suspected of dealing off the bottom of the deck. Cutting the fingers off a card cheat is not against the law. I hate to admit this, but I am afraid of him and a dozen others like him in this town.

At first, I despised the name "Kid." I do not look sixteen years old, I barely shave and certainly cannot grow a beard as is the fashion here. Even Jake is a full head taller than me, and he now has a fine reddish yellow beard. When I attended school I was always the smallest and scrawniest student, much as I am the smallest and scrawniest among these men here. I learned at school to make friends with Laurence Woodke, the biggest and dumbest boy in the room. By making him my friend I stayed out of trouble with the bullies because as soon as someone would pick on me, Laurence would walk up and hit his right fist into his left hand a few times. Most boys did not pick on me, at least not when Laurence was around. I am beginning to get used to the name "Kid," and perhaps it will prove to be a valuable asset. I shall be respectful and cautious of Lancelot Slade, Little Bill, Bar Keep Miller, and all the other wolves in this town.

Wednesday, July 10, 1861

Today I staked a claim up at the top of Buckskin gulch on the far side of a lake that I call Kite Lake for its shape, though it is more commonly known as Lake Minnehaha. I cut willow branches and set them in the ground every two paces over a hundred foot square. I shall record this claim tomorrow at the claims office, and no one else can legally dig there. I see no color when I dig, but I load ore onto my burros and carry it to the lake where I swirl the ore in my pan and usually find a few flakes of gold. I get less gold than those near the creek, but I stay out of the way of the "wolves." Erik and Glen Svensson, two Swedes with a claim upstream, have built a sluice box with wood purchased from me and can find more gold in an hour than those with pans get all day. This sluice is made of three long planks nailed together in a "u" shape to form an eight foot long trough with little cleats, called riffles, nailed on the bottom every few inches. They shovel ore on the top of the sluice box and allow water to flow through the box to wash away all light dirt and debris. Only rocks, black sand, and a few specks of gold remain behind in the riffles. The rocks are discarded and the gold dust and flakes can be removed with tweezers. Erik and Glen are regular purchasers of my merchandise and I like them. We don't understand each other well, but I think that they may let me run my ore down their sluice for a portion of any gold I find. It seems much easier than panning, and I won't get my feet as wet in the cold water.

Each day after I pull a few tiny specks of gold from my pan, I put the remaining black sand in a large whisky bottle. It contains a lot of shiny gold dots smaller than a grain of sand. I hear that I can sell this to an assayer who will then pour a heavy liquid called quick silver on that black ore to remove its gold. My bottle of black sand should be worth about ten dollars when full. Those specks large enough to separate from the black sand are put in one of those tiny green whiskey bottles that I hide under a rock on my claim. This gold dust can be spent the same as cash and many storekeepers have small scales to weigh this gold. A nugget the size of a dried kernel of corn can be traded for a dollar's worth of merchandise, though I have not found one that large. When this bottle is full of gold dust, it should weigh about five pounds. I will sell it, go home to Grass Creek and start that store, for it will be worth about a thousand dollars. I need to figure a method to find gold much faster. At the rate I am finding that mineral, the bottle will not be filled until my hair is gray.

Thursday, July 11, 1861

The area around this town never ceases to amaze me. While there is little in the way of green vegetation, the beauty of these enormous mountains is truly charming. The weather, however, is quite peculiar.

Back in Missouri, the warmest part of the house was the loft where I slept, and the haymow in the barn was scorching hot on a summer's day. Everyone knows that smoke rises because it is warm and that a flame is much hotter above it than beside it. So, why are these mountains so blessed cold? Some mornings I look to the mountain tops, and I can see fresh snow. Nearly every morning I can see my breath. Today while I was up at Kite Lake, the sky turned violent with angry dark gray clouds hastening not over but around the peaks scarcely a stone's throw above my head. Because of what some say is "electricity" in the lightning, my hair, as well as the hair on my animals, stuck straight out much like the fur of a frightened barn cat. Holly was nervous and wouldn't stop barking and the burros wanted to flee. I led them away from the lake and into a dry gulch because I have heard that such places can be a refuge from lightning, and I was sure that such a storm was soon to be upon us. Within minutes I was treated to a dazzling display of God's mighty power as bolt after bolt of exploding fire boomed around us. Then it started snowing; not the Christmas snows of Missouri, but pea-sized pellets similar to popped corn. These white kernels did not float through the air as snowflakes do, nor did they hurt like hail does, and the ground was soon covered with a soft, cold blanket of this strange cottony material. Within minutes the sun came out to melt this peculiar snow, and it was soon warm and calm as if nothing had happened.

The sun shines nearly every day. When one ventures into the sunlight, it is warm and pleasant, but standing in the shade of a tree minutes later can be down right chilly. If a man ventures outside without his hat, he can get the top of his scalp sunburned through even the thickest hair. Though it is now the middle of summer, the shady side of the trees and buildings still have large piles of snow which I collect to keep meat fresh.

Back home, I could see stars on many nights and I used to think that there must be a thousand of them. Here I see stars shining every night and I wonder if there are millions, and each glowing dot seems to be brighter and closer than the most brilliant shooting star the Missouri sky ever produced. The nights are quiet also: no forlorn howling of a distant coyote, no chirping of a cricket to remind us of how hot it is, not even the lowing of cows to fill the air. The only sound to be heard, so long as one keeps well away from the noise of the saloons and dance halls, is the quiet soothing sound of water as it trickles steadily along Buckskin Creek. I should like to build a cabin away from town a bit but within ear shot of that soothing trickle. Tomorrow after church Jake and I shall scout out such a place. He has learned a lot about carpentry and now owns some first-rate tools. With his skills and my help we can erect the finest dwelling in the area. He wants to build a house with plenty of headroom to walk around inside. He often complains about the ceiling heights in some of the homes and businesses here and jokes that "even the mice here are hunchbacked."

Back in Missouri every landmark, town, and body of water had a name. Here, with this area being inhabited for only a few months, very few places have a name everyone agrees on. With Richard's permission I shall write my weekly paragraph concerning the naming of places.

Monday, July 15, 1861

Normally I do not pay much attention to new arrivals in town, but today I found great excitement in a pair of wood cutters who entered town pulling a wagon load of lumber. It was the Watts brothers! They had started their timber business a few miles from here by the river where there are abundant trees for cutting. They came to town to sell their load of pine boards and ran into Jake as he was helping some French-speaking men from Canada build a shack. Their arrival could not have happened at a better time, for Jake and I are building our place by the creek and we could use their wood for the roof.

THE BUCKSKIN PRESS
July 18, 1861

Today we start a column on the naming of local landmarks. We shall start by officially choosing a name for this town that we all live in. Many call it "Buckskin Joe" after the miner who found gold here last year. Though few around here ever met him, his name was Joseph Higgenbottom and he wore leather clothing that he made himself. The name of the post office which will soon be here shall be "Laurette." It may be too late to change the name of the post office, but there is no rule that a post office must be the same as the town. Please present your vote to THE BUCKSKIN PRESS by noon Wednesday.

- by Thomas Boone

Wednesday, July 24, 1861

I now live in a house! I have not been writing much in the evening as Jake and I have been building our shack for the past two weeks. It is a modest place, about twelve feet by sixteen feet, made of logs set on a firm layer of stones held together with mud and lime. Each night for almost two weeks we would fell four trees, hack off the limbs, drag them to our site and build one course of logs for the house. The sloped ceiling inside begins at nearly seven feet and the peak is over ten feet off the floor. We can enter through the door without stooping over and can walk around freely without hitting our heads. Jake so often boasts now that our mice will not be hunchbacked that I demanded that he find a new saying or keep his mouth closed. I would rather think that our home will have no mice. We should get a cat, but I think that perhaps there is not a cat in town.

The roof is of boards purchased from the Watts brothers, layered in a lap fashion to keep the rain out. It has a door made from planks held to the house with leather straps. There are no windows, but we built a nice fireplace made of stones in the fashion of the foundation.

The chimney over the fireplace is made of wood boards, charred first and then coated on the inside with a heavy layer of mud and lime to make it fireproof, providing we make sensible fires. Though the place is small, I find great pleasure in being able to stand in the same area I sleep in for the first time in my life. The dirt floor poses no problems for we collect blood when we shoot an animal and pour it on the dirt to produce a black hard surface which is easy to sweep. It is also nice to not sleep in a tent and feel the breeze at night. We are just a few feet away from Buckskin Creek, and I can hear the trickle of water from inside the shack. Materials cost us twelve dollars, mostly for the wood and lime, and were well worth the price for we truly enjoy the comfort of being inside. Extra scraps of wood were used to make a little porch and a little house outside the door. This is where Holly sleeps to guard this humble home.

We made two beds out of pine boards so that we no longer have to sleep on the floor. I cut the canvas that until now we had used as a tent, in half and we each made a mattress stuffed with dried leaves and grass. It is very nice to not sleep on the cold hard ground.

Someday soon we shall cut a window into a wall, but as there is no glass to be bought, we will have to wait for that luxury. For now the two oil lamps serve us just fine to read by, and I have drawn plenty of sketches to hang on the wall as artwork, but my favorite drawing is one of Miss Silverheels that I bought for a dollar from Scotty Browne, who is a fine artist when he is sober.

With 74 votes in favor, we shall officially call our bustling town by the name of "Buckskin Joe." Coming in second place with 10 votes was the name "Gold Hill." Though "Laurette" will be the name of the post office, that name only got 3 votes.

Next week we vote on the name of the lake above town. Some from Minnesota call it "Lake Minnehaha," some from the South like the name "Dixie Lake," I like "Kite Lake" because of its shape. Please present your vote or other suggestions to: THE BUCKSKIN PRESS by noon Wednesday.

- by Thomas Boone

Wednesday, July 31, 1861

The Tabor store is finished, and today Jake and I helped Horace and Augusta fill the shelves with groceries and supplies. When it opens tomorrow, it will be the first store in town to sell its merchandise from within a single building instead of out of wagons, tents and shacks. The store is very nice and it is the first building in town to have wood floors which I expect will be swept very clean by Mrs. Tabor. If a shipment of glass ever arrives, the store will also have the first glass windows for there is a very large framed opening on each side of the entry door to let light in. The hinged shutters on the windows can be fully opened to allow light in and make the room very bright and cheery. With this new and pleasant store another layer of civilization has settled on our little city.

Jake has become not only good at carpentry but enjoys it so much that he will now partner up with the Watts brothers to build small shacks such as the one we live in. If the brothers can saw lumber fast enough, Jake thinks that he and a helper can build two small homes a week. They plan to sell them for twenty-five dollars to any newcomer who still has that much money remaining. Jake is saving money to build a boarding house and will start construction by this coming spring. He then will quit building cabins and run a place similar to his parents' hotel in Pigeon Creek. He wishes for his boarding house to be the first two-storied building in Buckskin Joe, and he will name it Jake's Place.

Thursday, August 1, 1861

Today, Mr. Tabor directed that I deliver a bag of apple cores two miles upstream from his store. What an unusual request. The Tabor Store sells apples, but they are nearly a year old, small, and rotten looking. Few buy apples, but Mrs. Tabor makes delicious apple pies and sells them for a half dollar a slice. I was tempted into buying a slice once. It smelled almost as good as my mother's pie but certainly not worth a half day's pay. Back home only pigs eat apple cores, and certainly no one would pay even a penny for a bag of this brown smelly garbage, but I was to deliver them to the Spanish arrastra and was to charge a man named Salvador two bits for yesterday's rubbish.

I had seen what was called by some to be "the Spanish Arrastra" in Buckskin Creek numerous times and had wondered by what power this smooth six foot diameter circle had been gouged out of the hard granite. The arrastra is perfectly round, carved, about a foot deep into the rock of the creek bed, and is very smooth. A chiseled hole about twelve inches deep has been somehow drilled in the center of this circle as if it were the hub of a great wheel. Until recently, no one knew why this circle was there. We only knew rumors of ancient Spanish gold seekers who somehow may have used this wheel to process gold. A few days ago an old Mexican came to the site and set up an ore-grinding operation. He brought with him only an aging burro and a few tools and implements. I had not yet visited his site for he is not one of Mr. Tabor's grubstakers and he does not speak a word of English, so today was the first I had witnessed this operation. Secured by means of a pine pole attached to the center of the arrastra, his ancient burro walks around and around in a circle dragging a flat rock. Many miners with no claim near water must look for gold in the white glassy rocks which seem to be the source of the gold around here. Until recently, they would smash this quartz with hammers or hard rocks and then pick the gold out with their fingers or tweezers. Now instead of hard labor smashing the quartz, they simply bring this ore to the arrastra to be ground into course sand by this man called Salvador, his burro, and that flat rock. He charges five cents to grind as much ore as a man may carry at one time. As water from the creek flows through the wheeled channel, dirt and light stones are washed away. The heavy sand that remains is then taken by the prospectors to the nearby water to be panned for loosened gold flakes.

The old Mexican is very fond of Orito, the burro, and helps pull the rock around and around in that cold wet circle. Perhaps Salvador even pulls harder than the burro does for he seems to not wish to tire his old companion. Once each revolution they each get their feet wet in that cold water, but neither seems to mind. Salvador talks to Orito as a mother talks to her baby though I do not understand his language. I have never seen a person show such fondness for any animal. Sometimes we talk to a horse or a dog, but never do we talk as if that animal were a person who understands what we are saying. Plowing a field is hard work, but no one back home would ever think of working harder than the horse. I realized that those apple cores were to be treats for this old Mexican's best friend. Perhaps Orito is his only friend.

I have never purchased treats for my burros; the thought has never even occurred to me. Though I have never seen such fondness for an animal, I do not find his affection offensive or even silly. I find the thought comforting. My father, and perhaps other men such as Father Dyer, would have a Bible verse condemning such love for a beast of burden. I regret that I seldom demonstrate such fondness for beast or man, and I sometimes wonder if I could show that kind of affection for a woman or for children. My mother has that ability.

I think of Becky often. Perhaps I shall write her another letter as soon as we get a postal office.

THE BUCKSKIN PRESS
August 2, 1861

By a vote of 56 to 32, the Lake above town will be named Kite Lake for its shape. Those from Minnesota vow to continue calling it Lake Minnehaha, but perhaps in a future contest we can find a good northern name for another site.

Next week we shall find a name for the peak rising above all others north of town. Some say that this mountain is taller than any other mountain on the continent. It is certainly taller than Pike's Peak for when you stand far below its summit, you can look level and see above that famous peak to the southeast.

Names this mountain is now known by and a few suggestions: Craggy Peak, Mount Vernon, Dixie Peak, Mount Jefferson Davis, Too Tall Mountain, Tin Cup Mountain, and my personal favorite - Goddess Peak. Please present your vote or other suggestions to: THE BUCKSKIN PRESS by noon Wednesday.

- by Thomas Boone

Thursday August 8, 1861

Jake has been bringing home slash from the sawmill operation, and we have been adding a vertical layer of these boards to the log walls of our house as an additional layer of protection from the cold weather we have been told is soon to come. With unsold papers from the Buckskin Press we have wallpapered over most of these boards

116

making the interior much brighter though we still do not have a window. I enjoy reading old copies of the paper when I am otherwise bored. Today a lonely miner named Rocken Rob who seemed desperate for something to read came by just to read the old newsprint and look at my sketches covering the walls. I would have loaned him a book, but I still do not own such a thing other than Grandfather's old Bible. Rocken Rob asked permission to stop by occasionally to read our walls, and we consented.

Saturday, August 10, 1861

Some weeks ago three surveyors arrived to map this area with the hope of finding a possible route for a railroad through here to the Pacific. With their instruments, they climbed the highest mountain they could find and determined that there was no easy path through the gold country. What they discovered was that the mountain they were on was not only the highest mountain in the area, it was perhaps the tallest mountain on the continent, for when they sighted their instruments on Pike's Peak they found themselves to be hundreds of feet higher than its summit. I have been trying to talk Jake into climbing with me to the top of that unnamed mountain and stake my claim on her. What an adventure it will be to be for at least a few minutes looking down on all the people in the nation. Today he finally agreed to my wish, and tomorrow morning we hike to the top of the world.

Monday, August 12, 1861

Jake and I climbed that mountain yesterday, and I did not write last night for I was much too exhausted. We were, for a few hours, higher above sea level than any other person in America. I wonder if we were closer to the sky than anyone else in the whole world, for who knows where a taller mountain may exist?

We began our morning much the same as my mornings usually begin, by walking the four mile hike to Kite Lake. Jake had wanted to ride Muffin, but I convinced him that she could not negotiate all the rocks and inclines that we would encounter, so we just took Adam along with us to carry our supplies as he is the most sure footed of my animals. After passing by the lake we left the path of the creek and began our ascent up a trail that seemed to lead nearly straight up. We passed miners far above the creek digging without the benefit of a stream in which to wash out the gold. These were men who, like Jake and I, arrived here too late to file a claim near water and too poor to buy one. A few of them had a burro to help carry their ore but mostly these men worked their solitary claims with only a pick, a shovel, and a few bags in which to carry their rocks to the lake or stream to be panned.

The trees started thinning out as we climbed ever higher and higher, and after a hike of only a half hour above the lake most signs of humans and animals had disappeared except for the occasional whistling of some unknown critter beneath the rocks and a few seemingly lost birds. I wondered why a bird would fly this high, for surely there is very little food up there for one to eat.

We soon came upon a grove of trees unlike any I had ever seen before and possibly the highest trees in the country, for there were no trees to be seen above this little grove. These pine trees were scarcely taller than I and had outstretched limbs which looked almost like human arms. These arms have surely been sculpted and twisted into contortions by years of harsh blowing winds, for even on a calm August day such as yesterday, it was a little breezy there. This little forest had a magical look to it and I could imagine elves and fairies dancing under a full moon beneath those outstretched and human-like arms. Lightning had struck some of the trees numerous times and

those mysterious trees had lived on to tell their stories as evidenced by ugly black scars on their twisted trunks.

Upward past that magical forest, the grass grew so sparse that surely no animal, not even a mountain goat, would climb this high up for nourishment. I was pleasantly surprised to find among the sparse blades of grass a few mountain flowers still proudly showing their colors of blue, yellow, white, and red. I thought of Becky and how she used to pick wild flowers for her hair as we walked. Jake was a fine companion, but I would rather have been walking with Becky while beholding the sights. Perhaps I could have been holding her hand.

As we continued our climb along a well traveled path, Jake asked, "Who made this path? Wasn't gold discovered here only a couple of years ago?"

"Indians," I replied. "Richard told me that Indians used to make spiritual trips to the tops of many mountains to communicate with 'The Great Spirit.' This must be one of their sacred mountains."

"I guess it's a good thing that Adam is carrying my gun," he said. "By the way, I can barely breathe. Did those Indians steal the air, or did it just vanish?"

He was not jesting about the missing air for we each fought for our breath as if we had just finished a foot race. Some say, "The air is thin in these here mountains," and thin is an understatement when approaching the summit of one of these fantastic peaks; it is not just thin, it is unbearably skinny. My lungs burned as we struggled ever upward along that well-worn path.

Soon, even the moss on rocks was left behind. There was no vegetation of any kind, nor insects on the ground, nor birds in the air. All that was left on that mountain were a few piles of snow slowly melting in the warm sunshine, a lot of loose rocks, Jake, me, Adam, and that well worn path.

We reached the summit at about noon. It was not a point as I had suspected but a level area large enough to play that game of base-ball on. I imagined hitting a ball from that diamond for it would surely have traveled for miles from this height. Jake and I beheld a sight from there that makes me feel, as Mrs. Hultgren used to say, "a poverty of language," as I try to write this, for it was the most magnificent view I had ever seen and the most spectacular panorama that I ever expect to see, should I never climb another mountain. There may be an artist somewhere who someday might paint this amazing scenery on a piece of canvas but he would never be able to capture the awe we felt at that moment. From up there we saw no signs of human destruction to the landscape or signs of any human activity at all, for that matter, for all we could see to the west was row after row of similar white capped peaks towering over thick dark green forests. We could follow with our eyes the paths of rivers as they began their thousand mile courses to the sea. We knew from our limited knowledge of geography that the rivers to the west flow a speedy downhill path to the Pacific Ocean, and those to the east begin a slower and lazier voyage to the Gulf of Mexico. To the east was that landmark we had journeyed west to find, Pike's Peak, and beyond that, stretching like an amber blanket for mile after endless mile until it reached the horizon, was that land we had a few months ago walked over to get here, that great vast plain we call the Great American Desert. I wondered just how far I could see, certainly at least a hundred miles or so. They say that you can see three territories from the top of a tall mountain such as this: Colorado, Utah, and New Mexico.

Richard once lent me a book that contains a poem that reads like this:

> "Lo, the poor Indian! Whose untutor'd mind
> Sees God in clouds, or hears him in the wind."

and I thought back to that Indian boy my father shot. I held my arms up to the sky, just as he had done two years ago and started chanting "Eeewa, eeewa oh," just as I remembered him doing. It felt good

120

and I could feel the August sun pleasantly warming my face in the otherwise chilly air, much as a warm fire feels good to the skin on a cold evening.

Jake laughed, "You're going to get struck by lightning," but he soon joined me in chanting with his arms stretched up as well. Then he began hopping around, dancing just as we had done as children when we pretended to be Indians. This time I laughed and joined in, and as Jake made drum sounds, I whooped, and we danced around that diamond in the sky until our lungs ached in that skinny air.

We stayed up there for perhaps an hour, tried with no avail to carve our names in the hard granite, but did manage to stake a claim by marking a one hundred foot square by placing rocks every two paces apart which I plan to record tomorrow. After eating a lunch of buffalo jerky, nuts and water and absorbing into our memories as much splendor as we could, we began our long descent down that well traveled path. As we neared that magical forest, the sky darkened and the hair on our heads stood out and felt as if charged with bees. Dark, fleet moving clouds flew, not above our heads, but directly at us, and seemingly through us, causing us to become immediately quite cold. My finger tips tingled as if about to discharge mighty bolts of lightning. I have been in sudden storms like this before, but this time there was no gully or gulch to hide in.

Jake yelled out through the howling wind, "I warned you about the lightning, but you wouldn't listen!"

I yelled back, "If this is to be my last adventure on this earth, I will personally thank God for allowing me a view of this world for a few minutes the way He sees it every minute of every day."

The only thing that struck us during that brief storm was a few stinging drops of very cold and icy rain against our faces. Soon the winds died down and the sun returned. Neither of us talked much for the next two hours as we continued our downhill walk home. We just reflected on all we had seen, heard, and felt.

Friday, August 30, 1861

Once a week Mrs. Tabor helps me load two baskets of what she calls "necessities" to peddle uphill to miners who live up above town. We balance this merchandise on each side of Eve, a chore she must hate for the noise these goods make as they rattle around. The "necessities" include not groceries or hardware, but grooming items such as combs, soap, and brushes, as well as cloth, needles, thread, matches and so forth. I even load empty flour sacks which I sell for ten cents a bag for the men to use or to cut up into patches for their clothing. She tells me the prices I must charge for these items and I am often surprised by the high costs which are many times what they would cost in Grass Creek. Though I know that she must make a fortune, and I am well aware that I make an additional ten percent, she instructs me to blame the prices on the high cost of shipping goods overland. When a man demanded to know why a card of five needles worth about a penny would cost him a dime, I felt a little foolish when I replied, "It's the high cost of freight."

I first heard the term "mining the miners" while still walking here from the East, but I had no idea that the riches to be found here have less to do with gold than with keeping these gold seekers supplied with their needs. Some men, indeed, find nuggets occasionally

122

that are worth large sums of money, but this money is often soon squandered on whiskey, gambling, or frolicking with women. I think that the Tabor Store must make enormous profits, but Augusta Tabor keeps a tight hold on the money, and she and Horace work hard and live humbly.

Sunday, September 1, 1861

Today I again went to church out on the street, but this service turned out a little different from the others. As usual, Father Dyer arrived by horseback at about noon. He always yells about the sins of our community, and most frequently hollers about the saloons, whorehouses, or gambling tables. Today, he immediately started preaching about the sinful dance halls. He told us that the Bible held that dancing or any contact with women other than in marriage is a sin. He preached that all dance halls with their wicked alcohol and women should be avoided altogether and prayed that God would strike these "houses of sin" with lightning so that they all would soon burn to the ground.

I usually stand close to Miss Silverheels and spend most of the service staring at her and admiring her beauty. As Father Dyer stood there in front of us yelling, I could see that Miss Silverheels was crying. Fortunately for me, I was carrying a clean handkerchief in my pocket. I quietly moved close to her and offered it to her to wipe her tears. "He's wrong, you know," I whispered as I handed it to her. She wiped her eyes and handed it back to me, but instead of just placing it in my hand, she gave my outstretched fingers a gentle squeeze.

"Thank you," she said.

I had not even noticed that the sermon was over and it was now time to sing. Miss Silverheels owns a little song book and offered to share it with me. Though I know every word of "Nearer My God to Thee," I pretended to need her hymnal and stood very close to her as we sang together. I sang very softly so to hear her glorious voice.

The service was soon over. I offered to walk Miss Silverheels home and she obliged. I was nervous and said very few words during our entire three or four minute stroll. I just beheld her beauty as we silently walked.

At the door to the Silver Slipper, she turned to me and said, "The world could use a whole lot more men like you, Mr. Tom…Thomas Boone," and then she gracefully entered and left me standing there in awe. I hung around the saloon for nearly an hour so I could catch glances of her inside dancing, and indeed I saw her on three occasions through the opened door, dancing in that scarlet and revealing dress.

Monday, September 2, 1861

Did man evolve from the ape?

Since Richard Hamilton moved to town, I have had plenty to read as he brought with him about twenty books and dozens of old newspapers. The book that I am reading right now is Charles Darwin's book <u>On The Origin of Species</u>. It was published just last year and has created quite a stir on this continent as well as in Europe. Darwin's book theorizes that all animals have developed over long periods of time and are still changing today through what he calls "natural selection" to meet whatever changes in climate or food these animals encounter. Only those creatures strong enough to withstand a change in living circumstances survive to create stronger offspring.

Back home on the farm our mules were the biggest and strongest of any such beast of burden for miles around. I am certain that the reason for our impressive mules was that father bred only the biggest and strongest donkeys to the biggest and strongest horses. I have noticed that the hair on my burros is longer and thicker here in the mountains than it ever was in Missouri where the temperatures are warmer. Are they adapting to this climate? Because Number 4 has the thickest coat, would it not make sense that her offspring would have thick coats as well?

I was taught that the world was created in seven days and all animals were created, I believe, on day six. This new idea of animals evolving over time runs contrary to what I was taught, but it makes sense. Because I was taught that animals were created in a single day, I should not believe that animals "evolved" …but I might be accepting of the idea. Though Darwin did not write it, I have heard the rumors that some think that man evolved from the ape, as well. Richard says, "Well, of course we did." This idea makes sense to me, as well, but I shall not make my views known until I have thought about this blasphemous concept for some time.

Richard told me that in Greek mythology, from thousands of years ago, a creature called "the Sphinx" sat outside of a place called Thebes and asked a riddle of all travelers who passed by. If the traveler failed to solve the riddle, then the Sphinx killed him. If the traveler answered the riddle correctly, then the Sphinx would kill herself.

The riddle: What goes on four legs in the morning, on two legs at noon, and on three legs in the evening?

After a lot of travelers were killed, a man named Oedipus solved the riddle, and the Sphinx killed herself.

The solution: Man, who crawls on all fours as a baby, walks on two legs as an adult, and walks with a cane in old age.

Richard says that the Bible was also written thousands of years ago and perhaps "day" could mean a long period of time. He believes in this thing called "evolution" and says that the world was created in seven eras. This idea makes sense to me, but it is not how I was taught. I do not know what to believe. I wonder what Becky would think? She might say, "Where are the rules written that say we have to believe all that we are taught?"

Tuesday, September 3, 1861

Today when I went to Buckskin Creek to get water for the animals there was barely a trickle running and I had to dig a hole in the stream bed just to fill my bucket.

When I loaded my burros at the store Mr. Tabor told me not to bother with taking lumber or anything but a little food as there was a commotion somewhere up stream. I passed mining operation after operation and sluice after sluice but there was no sign of prospectors anywhere nor was there much water in the gulch.

I kept plodding along without seeing a soul until I was about a mile from the lake. In a clearing by the stream about a hundred angry men, many carrying firearms, were yelling at about twenty armed men crouching behind a stone wall. Those men, all unfamiliar to me, were pointing rifled muskets at the angry crowd.

"You have no right to dam the creek," yelled a furious Erik Svensson in a heavy accent and one hundred voices echoed his opinion. Other men were yelling, "You cannot claim ownership to water!"

Whenever anything evil happens around here it seems that those men who frequent the Wolves' Head Saloon are involved and sure enough Lancelot Slade, Little Bill, and four other armed men soon arrived on horseback carrying a sign that read: **Timberwolf Ditch Company.** They nailed it to a tree and Slade said in a very loud and commanding voice, "From now on water will be purchased from us and will be delivered to your claim by a ditch built by us and paid for by you!"

"No one owns the water!" "I'll blow that dam sky high!" "Do you have a dam to stop the flow of blood once I put some lead in your ass?" were some of the comments I heard as I hung around. In about twenty minutes I went home afraid of the twenty armed men pointing their rifles at us in the crowd. It was well after dark when I heard the sounds of the saloons but it was not music and revelry, it was the angry shouting of dozens of furious men.

Wednesday, September 4, 1861

This morning I awoke to the sound of thunder but no rain came, nor were there clouds in the sky. Buckskin creek is again flowing but

126

I shall not make my rounds. I will tell Mr. Tabor that I need this day to make repairs to my pack saddles and I will do just that.

THE BUCKSKIN PRESS
September 5, 1861

This Tuesday past witnessed unfortunate undertakings a few miles upstream from our fair city. It seems that a few men with claims on both sides of Buckskin Creek decided that since the water flowed through their claims, it was theirs to do with as they wished, and through the night of September 2 about twenty hired men from the town of Park City constructed a dam across the stream. This action created a lot of heated words from men with claims downstream who rely on this water for their mining operations. At about 3 o'clock Wednesday morning the dam was destroyed by an exploding keg of gun powder, and Buckskin Creek now flows again. No one has yet come forth to claim responsibility for the destruction of this dam. As we currently have no means to enforce laws here this destruction will likely not be investigated. We ask that men on both sides of this issue refrain from violence until this issue is resolved peacefully.

As we have no laws here concerning the ownership of water, a meeting has been called for tomorrow afternoon at 2 o'clock on the street in front of this newspaper to draft rules of conduct for rights to the flow of water in Buckskin Gulch. Any man with a recorded claim will have the right to vote and say his peace.

- Richard Hamilton

Sunday, September 8, 1861

With great courage, I stood by Miss Silverheels again at church. She smiled when I approached and positioned myself beside her. Though I know the words to all the hymns, I again shared her songbook. I also shared my Bible with her and secretly hoped Father Dyer would yell something that would make her to be in need of my clean and folded handkerchief. I stood so close to her that I could smell her perfume, and again I had trouble listening to the sermon, but did not care; for dreaming of Miss Silverheels is much more pleasant than listening to the fire and brimstone that loudly spews from Father Dyer's mouth.

Friday, September 20, 1861

What a splendid day today was for living in this bustling little city on the top of the world. The sun was bright and warm but a pleasant cool breeze kept the day from becoming hot like it does back home. Though only the third week in September, all the aspen leaves have turned a brilliant yellow that quiver in this pleasing breeze and seem to boast their glory against the deep blue sky. I cannot imagine a better place to live on a September day such as this.

THE BUCKSKIN PRESS
September 21, 1861

Men departing this gold camp by way of horse, wagon or coach are a daily occurrence here. Men departing by means of a coffin to the cemetery above town are so commonplace that we seldom mention their exodus in this newspaper. Births are entirely a different matter. Today we will not talk about the naming of landmarks, we will talk about the name of a baby.

Born to recent arrivals from Iowa, prospector Henry Stenner and his wife Hetti, is a healthy daughter. This baby girl is the first child to be recorded in the county archives, and perhaps the first white baby born west of the supply cities on the plains. Welcome to Buckskin Joe: Emma Charlene Stenner!

- by Thomas Boone

Friday, September 27, 1861

Jake turns eighteen this coming Monday and wishes a gathering. Not only does he wish to invite friends over, he wants to celebrate with music such as we enjoyed on the plains and he thinks that the addition of spirits will make the night more festive. I am against having whiskey in the house, but I still wonder why an evening gets

128

livelier with the addition of alcohol. Some evenings on our journey here to Colorado got quite merry and the sounds outside of a saloon are of laughter and song.

Jake has been a good friend here in Buckskin Joe. Ever since his bad experience on the trail, he has lost much of his former boisterous attitude. He has learned that money comes from hard work and he has certainly toiled for his pay. While I walk about fifteen miles a day and come home weary, Jake works much harder. He spends much of his day with an axe in his hand shaping logs so that they stack tightly upon each other. While I wish to go back to Missouri some day with wealth, Jake likes the mountains and wishes to stay. For leisure he hops on Muffin and takes long rides to explore new places. He carries his Hawken rifle on his lap hoping to chance upon an elk, buffalo or mountain sheep, but comes home satisfied when none is encountered, having just enjoyed a ride in the mountains.

Tomorrow, I will walk down to the Fair Play Diggings to purchase a few bottles of wine as a gift for Jake. He certainly deserves a good present. As far as I know, whiskey is not mentioned in the Bible, but wine is. I see no harm in honoring Jake's request.

Tuesday, October 1, 1861

I shall never drink alcohol again.

Old Tom

The evening of Jake's eighteenth birthday was a grand affair, and I look back upon that night with fond memories. I had come back from the settlement on the edge of the South Park Plains with three bottles of peach wine made in Michigan and three bottles of red grape wine made in St. Louis.

Jake had taken the day off to go hunting and fishing. He came back with a small deer and two trout. Near sundown the Watts brothers, each with a pocket mouth organ, stopped by to celebrate as did, Richard from the Buckskin Press, his driver, Mike Armstrong, and a half dozen miners I knew but not well. Smilen George arrived well after dark with his fiddle.

We built a very large fire outside, roasted the venison, fried the fish, and played and sang every song we knew while passing the wine bottles around the fire. I do not remember falling asleep, but I awoke shivering beside the glowing embers of the evening's fire. Jake, the Watts brothers, and two miners were all asleep and shivering as well. The next day was a miserable day for me as I could not hold food or water down and my head felt as if it were splitting in two.

I did not drink another drop of alcohol for some time but eventually I acquired a taste for fine red wine when consumed in moderation. Despite my hangover and embarrassment for getting drunk I look back upon that evening as one of the happier evenings of my early life in Colorado.

The smell of peach wine nauseates me to this day.

Sunday, October 6, 1861

For five Sundays now, I have stood by Miss Silverheels at church sharing her hymnal and my Bible, and for five Sundays, I have walked her to her home at The Silver Slipper. She is pleasant to talk to, but I always find words hard to say because I am so thrilled to be in her company. When we get to her door, she turns to me, thanks me for walking her home and extends her hand to me. She grasps my hand and smiles as if I am her favorite younger brother. I accept her gentle grip as if it were a gift from an angel. With the exception of a few glimpses of her dancing through an open door, I do not see her for another week.

Monday, October 21, 1861

It snowed today. I do not ever remember even a light snow this early in the year back in Missouri. I made my route today despite nearly a foot of the deep white powder. While I struggled with every step I took, the burros traversed the slippery powder with no difficulty. Again I was amazed at how six burros could leave only two sets of footprints. I left no foot prints in the snow, either, I just left two lines behind me much like the furrows in a freshly plowed field to remind others of my struggle. I came upon two miners from Minnesota. They had fashioned what they called "snow shoes" out of willow branches and walked easily on top of the snow. I also met Father Dyer on the trail, though what he was doing up there I do not know. Strapped to each of his feet was a six foot long plank of wood with the end turned up. He was sliding on top of this snow with ease with the help of poles in his hands. He called these contraptions "snow shoes" as well.

I collected some willow branches from near the lake and brought them home with me. The Minnesota snow shoes look simple to make and easy to walk in. Tonight I will make a pair to strap to my boots, and tomorrow I shall walk on top of the snow with ease.

Wednesday, October 30, 1861

Another day of danger and another night I shall not sleep. I get weary of having a weapon pointed at my face, but it has happened again. Since starting on this quest I have had a weapon pointed at me six times, but for the first time I thought that my life was about to end. I am now fearful that my days on this earth are short.

As I was returning to town after a trek up to Kite Lake and back, I heard a woman screaming for help. I could see Jake and four others all running through the slushy snow toward the sound of the commotion and all five were carrying their firearms. Jake yelled for me to help him, so I tied my pack train to a tree, grabbed my scattergun, and followed.

The scream apparently came from near the Wolves' Den. As we approached the sound of the shrieking, we could see Lancelot Slade pulling Miss Silverheels by the arm. She was wearing that revealing scarlet dress and those silver slippers, and her dress was torn. I do not know whether it was from being in the cold air without her jacket or from fear, but Miss Silverheels was violently shaking.

"Miss Silverheels, is this man bothering you?" Jake yelled.

She nodded, and Slade pulled his revolver out of his pocket with his free hand and pointed it between Jake's eyes.

"Mind your own business boy. This 'so called' lady owes me a favor. Since her arrival she has done nothing but tease me with her smiles and flirting."

"She owes you nothing." Jake calmly said while staring down the muzzle of that revolver. "There are five of us and one of you. Let her go, and there will be no trouble."

"Look behind you," Slade warned, and as we turned around, we saw Little Bill and four other men from the Wolves' Den pointing various weapons at our backs. "They all get a turn after me and there is nothing you can do to stop it." He paused a second, "Now drop your guns and go home."

None of us obeyed that order, we just stood there frozen quietly in fear and anger. Jake bravely kept staring at the six shooter but said nothing.

Suddenly behind us we heard the unmistakable blast of a shotgun followed by the pattering sounds of lead pellets as they landed on nearby rooftops and rocks.

"You go home Slade" roared Big Al the owner of the Silver Slipper as he quickly walked to the scene from behind the Silver Slipper with a shotgun in one hand and a revolver in his other. "This gun has two barrels. I can shoot the ass off a skunk at twenty yards, and you are most definitely a skunk of the lowest order!"

"No one has to die," Lancelot Slade calmly said. "This woman just needs a few lessons on how to behave like a lady. You can't shoot all six of us."

"I don't intend to shoot anyone but you, Slade…just you," and Big Al aimed that shotgun at Slade's heart.

For a few seconds no one said a word. Big Al stood there like a statue and pointed his weapon at Slade's chest. Slade kept his revolver pointed between Jake's eyes while Jake stood motionless looking down the barrel of that revolver. In front of the Wolves' Den, Slade's five cohorts kept their weapons pointed at those of us who had run to Miss Silverheels' rescue. I stood stationary as a tree quaking in the breeze with my finger on the trigger as did the four others. With all the bravery I could muster I looked Slade squarely in the eyes. If anyone pulled a trigger, a lot of us would surely die.

Then the big German bartender started counting backwards, and I started praying, for my chances of living through this did not seem too good. "Ten…nine…eight…"

When the count got to three Slade calmly said, "Very well." The malicious gambler's face was now beet red. He let loose of Miss Silverheels' arm and turned around to walk back to the Wolves' Den while his five friends followed walking backwards with their weapons pointing at us. As he reached the door of the saloon, he turned around and yelled, "I wouldn't walk alone if I were any of you. I sometimes shoot rats when I'm bored and I see a lot of rats here today."

No one responded as we watched the men disappear behind the door.

Miss Silverheels tearfully thanked us and ran to Big Al. He put a protective arm over her shoulder and walked her back to the Silver Slipper. The five of us who had come to the rescue of our maiden followed closely behind with our fingers still on the triggers of our firearms and turning around frequently to see if anyone was following.

Now I lie again fearfully awake as I did when we rescued Martha and Mason, but this time I am afraid of a man who I seem to encounter every day and who is feared by many. I think that Mr. Slade would gladly shoot any of us if he could perform the act without getting caught. Jake suggests that we walk in groups from now on and carry our weapons in our hands. I agree. I sometimes wish that lawmen could be hired to bring order to this rowdy settlement. Even more so, I wish Slade and his wolf pack would just leave this town or otherwise vanish from this earth.

Saturday, November 2, 1861

The sun comes out and shines brightly every day but the snow lingers. More snow fell yesterday, and I wonder if the ground will remain covered until spring. I made snow shoes out of the willow branches and walked clumsily on top of the snow, but they fell apart in two days. I normally do not like to purchase something that I can make myself, but I bought two snow shoes so I can continue my route up to the lake with relative ease. I traded two pea sized nuggets to one of those Minnesotans named Jacobson for a pair of well built shoes. They are tightly woven of willow branches and have a leather strap to hold them in place on my feet. "Big Jake," as he likes to be called, seems to be a nice man. He doesn't say much, he just nods his head a lot and smiles. With a little practice I can now walk on top of the snow instead of plodding through it.

Though the ground is covered in snow, men still continue to look for gold. Buckskin Creek still trickles along, and the days are quite pleasant when the sun comes out. Hundreds of men trampling in the snow have created paths which are easy to travel. I pack my snow shoes on Eve and only put them on when I get off the paths.

November 4, 1861
Dearest Becky,

We finally have a post office so you can now send letters. Mr. Dodge got his wish to name the postal address of this mining area after his wife and daughter. He is now the postmaster here and manages the office from the front room of a new two-room cabin that Jake built. Mr. Dodge served with Winfield Scott in some battles in Mexico and still has his old army jacket, a drum, and a fifteen-year-old American flag. Each morning he puts on that old jacket, runs the flag up a tall pine pole and salutes it. Sometimes he can talk someone into beating that drum as the flag rises slowly up that pole. He then goes into his cabin and does whatever a postmaster does. The governor here has called out for the towns and mining districts to begin forming militias in case there is any trouble from the Confederates or Indians, and Mr. Dodge is trying desperately to form a company of soldiers. Some days after the flag raisings about twenty men remain to march up and down the street with rifles on their shoulders. They call themselves "The Buckskin Brigade." and even have a flag made out of elk skin. I sometimes watch, but I do not participate.

Neither Jake nor I have received any news from Grass Creek in the half year we have been gone. I hear that all of Missouri is in turmoil with Confederate sympathizers fighting Union sympathizers. They say that pro-slave men burn down the farms of abolitionists and that Union men burn down farms and homes of slave holders. I know that your father, like my father, is very much against the institution of slavery. I hope all is well in the Grass Creek area. I pray that you are safe from all this nonsense that is taking place all over our country.

If you got my last letter, you know that I am doing well here in the mountains of Colorado. I find very little in the way of gold so I now know that I will not return by winter, as planned; nor will I return a wealthy man. I am, however, making much more money than I would in Grass Creek, and I am saving it in a jar hidden where no one can find it. If I continue to save as I have been, I should return to Grass Creek by the 4th of July and I may have enough money to start that dry goods store, though I might have to start with less inventory than I would have liked. Jake wants to stay forever in the mountains and build and operate a hotel here. He likes the sunshine and the cool weather and like most of the men here needs only a good woman at his side to make this place a perfect area in which to live.

Holly has turned into the finest friend an animal can be. She stands taller than my knees and her coat has turned to a fine dark brown color which shines in the sun. She only barks when she senses danger or when she feels my burros aren't walking fast enough and sits at my feet when I am not walking. She is the envy of the town and I thank you again for the fine gift you gave me those many months ago.

The longer I am away, the more I miss you. I wish we would have begun our Sunday walks years ago instead of wasting our time climbing trees. I wish that you lived here in Buckskin Joe, but I know that wish can never be fulfilled. Some men carry one of those new fangled tin types of their girl back home. I wish I had your likeness wearing that pretty blue dress on a piece of tin. I would have it in a frame on the shelf next to my bed and talk to it before I went to sleep each night.

The weather here is already cold, and I have trouble writing with these numb fingers, so I will end this now and write again soon.

Warmly,
Thomas Boone,
Laurette, Colorado Territory.

THE BUCKSKIN PRESS
November 5, 1861

This civil war, as some like to call it, nearly came to the town of Buckskin Joe this Tuesday past. It seems that when Postmaster Henry Dodge marched out of his home that early morning carrying the American flag proudly cradled in his arms, the flag of the Confederacy was already boldly flying over our dear town. Mr. Dodge immediately went back inside his dwelling and emerged in about a minute with a fully loaded flintlock musket from the Mexican war. To remove the offensive flag, he walked up to the flagpole and tugged on the rope, but the flaxen cord had been cut and three pieces of it fell on Henry's head. Men standing on the opposite side of the street began laughing and taunting Mr. Dodge causing his face to redden with rage. On the other side of the street pro Union men were yelling to have the flag shot down or burned at once. Before any fires could be lit or shots fired in anger, a group of men led by Reverend Dyer arrived at the scene. Reverend Dyer yelled "Blessed are the peacemakers" to the crowd and some of the largest and strongest men hoisted the smallest member of our community, Thomas "Kid" Boone, up on their shoulders to cut the brazen flag down. By the time the ordeal was over, perhaps thirty or more men were at the scene with loaded weapons. Though everyone in town knows who the Southern and Union sympathizers are, few openly took sides that morning and no shots were fired. No man has yet claimed ownership of the Confederate flag and Mr. Dodge disposed of it in his own manner.

The flag pole to this day has not been repaired and no colors, North or South have flown over Buckskin Joe in almost a week.

- Richard Hamilton

BUCKSKIN PRESS
Editorial

Some weeks ago the Colorado Territorial Legislature was petitioned to have this town of Buckskin Joe (or Laurette) designated as the Capital of the Colorado Territory. The thinking is that this town best serves as the hub of all mining activity in the state and is more centrally located than the current capital of Colorado City, eighty miles by bad roads and rocky trails to the southeast. Other towns in consideration are two small towns on the plains: Denver City and Golden City. Each of these towns is serviced by the Overland Trail, making communication with the East more reliable, but Denver City and Golden City are well away from the mining and the resulting population boom. To those of us wishing for this town to be designated as the capital of our new territory, this incident has proven to be somewhat of an embarrassment. We here at the BUCKSKIN PRESS wish that all of our citizens remain respectful of each other and pull no more shenanigans such as this flag incident.

- Richard Hamilton, Editor

FLAG OF THE CONFEDERACY IN 1861

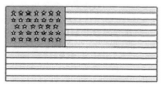

FLAG OF THE UNION IN 1861

CHAPTER 8

The Pox

Old Tom

    As I piece together this journal, I find an important chapter is missing. I have always maintained a daily journal with few exceptions, but one long lapse in writing came during that cold winter of 1861, nearly fifty years ago when I lived high up in the mountains during the gold rush. One reason for not writing was that my fingers could not properly grasp a pen in that cold cabin that I shared with my friend Jake. It was downright freezing in there. So cold, in fact, that a pot of coffee warming over the evening fire was frequently frozen by morning.

We had built this cabin, Jake and I, on evenings after already putting in ten hours of labor at our jobs. Within a few days we had constructed a small but sturdy log dwelling about twelve feet square. Though not much larger than our hen house in Missouri, it was our home, and a certain satisfaction comes from living in something one has built. It had only one room with a dirt floor and a fireplace. For privacy we hung a couple of elk hides to separate our sleeping areas. The only natural light came in through the open door for we had no glass for windows. The two oil lanterns that I brought from Missouri were burning whenever we were inside, and I read and re-read my Bible daily under them for other than the books I borrowed from Richard, the Good Book was the only reading material available. Our home was snug and cozy until winter came, and winter in the high country comes early ...in mid-October, as I remember. From then on, all available energy, outside of working, was spent on keeping warm by chopping wood, building fires, shoveling snow and drinking hot dandelion tea or coffee. We heated rocks on the fire and arranged them under our bunks to help keep us warm through the night. It helped a little.

But it was not only the cold that kept my journal blank during that winter of ice and snow; it was what we called back then "the pox." Some claimed that the pox was brought to town by Negroes, many claimed it was Indians, most blamed Mexican sheepherders but no one knew for certain because the first to get the disease were the regulars at The Wolves' Den. As Negroes were not allowed in saloons, and no Indians or Mexican sheepherders were within fifty miles, the disease was probably brought in by any one of the newcomers who arrived to the camp on a daily basis. No matter the origins, panic instantly spread throughout the camp.

Snow already covered the landscape that cold November, but at least two hundred of us attended an outdoor meeting, being careful

140

not to stand too close to one another for fear of contracting the disease. No one knew then exactly how smallpox spread, but we did know that it was very contagious. There was no doctor in town to advise us, but a few men were knowledgeable about it. The disease came from close contact, so a place like a saloon was a likely spot to acquire it. Everyone was urged to vacate the area at once, but Erik Svensson, the Swede, was nervous about claim jumpers and yelled out, "I'm a stayen!" About a hundred other voices yelled "So am I!" It was agreed that women and children should re-locate to someplace far away, such as Denver, and that those with wagons should help them move. While everyone should have departed the town as advised, few did; almost every male in town stayed to protect his claim. As I rarely got sick and did not frequent bars, I too, chose to remain, and though he had no claim to protect, Jake also refused to leave.

Smallpox begins with aches and fever. Within a few days a rash on the face or neck will appear. The rash soon turns into ugly and very painful blisters that resemble bellybuttons, and by then a person is so sick that wishing for a quick death seems to be the only reasonable way to deal with the wretchedness of this disease. One in three gets that wish to die. I, too, wanted to end my misery this way, but I survived. I survived with scars all over my body which are easy to see and scars deep within which I hide. It is the scars within that have prevented me from writing this story for all these years, but I remember the details of that cold winter as if it happened yesterday. I shall write as straight forward as I am able.

Jake and I went about our daily chores as usual, but winter presented many additional challenges. A fire had to be built each morning just to get the temperatures in our cabin to above freezing. As Buckskin Creek was frozen, I had to thaw snow to provide water for the animals. I had purchased some South Park hay from George Mills and kept it in a covered pile behind the cabin but had to shovel snow away each morning just to get a few handfuls for the burros. My socks were worn thin. I did not have proper flannels to wear under my clothing. My hat did not cover my ears, and I was cold all of the time.

The hair on my burros had grown long to keep them warm and they didn't seem to notice the extreme cold, but I certainly did.

I still ran my burro train each day as there were prospectors up there that needed supplies and I needed the money this trade brought. It took more effort to climb up to Kite Lake and back in foot-deep snow, so I had no time for working my claim. Digging in the frozen earth and then breaking ice in the lake to pan the ore by this time was much too painstaking a job for what little gold I found. To prevent contact with the disease I stayed a proper distance from the pros-pectors, and they stayed a respectful distance from me. I laid their supplies on the snow, and they, in turn, threw their tokens or money to me which I quickly put in a canvas sack. Other than Jake, the only person I came in contact with was Mr. Tabor as he helped me to pack supplies and grub each morning on my burros. We were careful not to get too close to each other.

The saloons remained open, and some men still frequented them.

Within a week of that first case, there were a dozen cabins and two boarding houses with a red handkerchief nailed to the door. This was the accepted way to identify a pox house. Once you got the pox, you suffered alone, for surely no one would enter to give you aid. Word had been sent to Denver that we needed nurses and that we were willing to pay for the care they could give, but none came.

One frigid morning about two weeks into the plague I awoke first to light the fire. I quickly had a nice blaze going, stood close to the flames, but just could not stop shaking. I hurt everywhere. I had been shivering, aching, and not feeling well for two days, and hoped that it was just the cold weather. Nevertheless, I made a pot of coffee and yelled at Jake to get up. He didn't answer; he just lay on his mat shivering. "I'm sick," he moaned. I looked at him and his face was covered with sores; not the kind you get when you are young, but large fiery red blisters. I said nothing, just grabbed my coat and went outside to feed the animals. Jake kept his horse at the livery, but my six burros were corralled behind the house with Holly always nearby in her little house to protect them. I fed them extra hay, grain and water, and then carried at least a week's worth of firewood inside and placed it on the floor next to the fire. For the first time in her life, I let Holly inside, fed her, and placed a bucket of water on the floor. Before going back to bed I went to the door and nailed my handkerchief to it for all to see. I would not go outside again for some time, for being in public with the pox could result in a bullet to the head and I could feel a rash on my neck.

Jake and I lay on our mats throughout the day, sleeping when we could, but got sicker with each passing hour. Jake always got his new symptoms a few hours before me and always seemed to be much more ill. The shivering would not stop though I had all my blankets, canvas, and clothing piled on top of me. The pox sores deepened and were very painful. We talked some. We agreed that if one of us were to die, that the other could keep all of his possessions, including animals. We did not write this down for we were too weak to do so. Any money left after burial would be sent back to our parents. I willed my Bible to Father Dyer so that he could have two Bibles at his services. Whenever I felt the strength, I put another log on the fire, but by evening that power no longer existed. Morning eventually came, I could tell by the light coming through the cracks between the boards, but I had not the strength to arise to build the fire or feed the animals. I just lay there shivering. I slept as often as I could; so did Jake.

Holly awoke me by barking furiously at the back wall, but I could not move. I heard Lancelot Slade outside yelling "These burros will die without being fed." We were too weak and sore to respond. "Very well, I shall take them as mine, since you boys are so irresponsible." We only heard the sounds of the animals being led away. Had Holly been outside, Mr. Slade might not have dared approach, or he might have shot her to protect himself, but I didn't care. Though Slade was the vilest man in the camp, I found comfort in not having to worry about my burros.

I was certainly going to die, and even an evil man such as Lance-lot Slade would feed my animals to keep them alive and healthy for resale.

At mid-morning a soft tap came to the door. I moaned but found no strength to answer. The door opened and Miss Silverheels silently walked in. Had I not been in my condition, this visit would have been the highlight of my young life for here in my modest cabin was the goddess of my desires. When I awoke suddenly from a dream as young men are prone do, it was Miss Silverheels who had inspired that dream. I did not care that she was perhaps six to eight years older than I for she was just so beautiful and enchanting.

Miss Silverheels was dressed in a black mourning dress complete with a veil. Most women do not own such an outfit unless tragedy has struck her immediate family. I suspect she wore this clothing, especially the veil, as a sort of nurse's uniform. She removed her snow covered leather boots at the door and put on perhaps the only soft shoes she owned, those silver dancing slippers. "Please, stay away," I whispered but she just closed the door behind her and smiled. "I'm here to help you get well Mr. Tom...Thomas Boone."

"You may call me Kid; I like the name now," I whispered.

"A brave man such as you is no kid, Mr. Tom, Thomas Boone." She looked at the painting of her on the wall and smiled. "Mr. Lewis is a brave man, as well, and you both know fine art when you see it."

Soon the door opened again and a Negro man entered carrying a pot of soup, a water pail and some clean cloths. I didn't know the name of the small man who lived in a tiny shack by the creek and did laundry, but everyone referred to him as China Mary. Miners from California had given him this name because laundry there had been a task performed by women or by Chinese men.

China Mary built a fire and placed the pot of soup on a hook over it to warm. He let Holly outside for a few minutes, filled her water bucket and fed her. As he did the heavier chores, Jake and I were washed softly by Miss Silverheels with warm water and a clean cloth and then oil was gently applied to our sores. Though we were not hungry or thirsty, she coaxed us into a few sips of the now warm porridge. I protested, "Miss Silverheels, you will catch the disease."

"No matter, Mr. Boone, Big Al has the pox, too. I take care of him, so why not you as well?" She stayed perhaps fifteen minutes and left as quietly as she came. Near sunset, and twice daily for the next two weeks, the visit was repeated. She fed us, cleaned us, emptied our pans, fed Holly, and helped us write our wills. China Mary worked silently in the background to help her quicken the process. The only joy during those two dreadful weeks was her two brief daily visits.

It was on a Sunday during Miss Silverheels visit that I saw that she was crying as she tended to my sores. "Why do you weep?" I asked.

"Too many good men are dying," she responded. "Big Al was a good man; your friend Jake was among the best, and just a lad."

"What do you mean? Is Jake dead?"

She nodded and said nothing but a tearful, "I'm sorry," finished her routine and quietly left. I was alone now, probably dying, and was now forced to suffer grief in solitude. Jake had died on the other side of that elk hide and I had been unaware of his plight. I had not even said goodbye. We had been companions since we were small boys. Though some of his actions were annoying to me, he was my only friend here in Buckskin Joe and perhaps the best friend I ever had. An hour later, Miss Silverheels returned, followed by two black men with bowed heads. "I have paid them to bury Jake," she said softly. "We will hold a service when you get better."

They wrapped Jake in his blanket, placed his body like so much meat on a board, and carried him silently out of the cabin.

"I will not be getting better," I whispered to Miss Silverheels as she followed silently behind Jake's lifeless body, and then I was alone again.

The next few days were the most miserable ones of my life in that dark and lonely cabin. I lay there alone wishing that I could end my misery, and dying seemed to be my best option. I was sick, I was sad and I was lonely. The only respite from my despair was the two brief daily visits by Miss Silverheels.

While applying oil to my sores a week later she assured me, "You are improving, Mr. Tom...Thomas Boone."

"No, I am not. Bury me next to Jake."

She smiled. Then I got a boldness that I had never asserted before. "Miss Silverheels, I have never been with a woman or even seen one for that matter. Some say that for a fee of a few dollars you will give a dance that shows more than the tops of your knees."

She stood silently and listened.

"I am aware that this is a rude request, but I need to know what all the fuss is about before I die. There are twenty silver dollars in a can on that shelf."

"Every lonely miner in town with a few dollars in his pocket has asked me that, and every lonely miner has been refused that request. Sorry, my brave friend, I'm just a dance hall girl and nothing more."

She stood there a few seconds looking at me with sadness in her eyes and motioned for China Mary to leave. "You are one of a very few men in this town who has treated me with respect," she said as she moved close to the warm blazing fire. "A young man's dying wish should be granted." To my great surprise and delight, she then slowly removed all her clothing with the exception of the veil and those silver slippers and performed one of her graceful dances while humming a tune as I watched. I had seen sketches of unclothed women, brought

146

to school by friends, and had an idea of what a woman looked like, but I did not know that the sight of a naked woman would produce such a reaction in me, especially in my condition. I did not know that a woman's skin could appear that soft, or that her body could be so shapely and tender. Though in my mind, I was most certainly about to die, my body was reacting in a very living manner. Surely, Miss Silverheels could sense my reaction, for the sadness she had been showing soon changed into a soft smile. She gracefully danced for a good five minutes in the firelight of that otherwise dark cabin.

Miss Silverheels then kissed me on the cheek while still unclothed. As she re-dressed she assured me, "You're not dying, my friend. A fine young man, such as you, must have left a pretty girl behind. Keep that twenty dollars, go home to her, and let this day be our little secret."

I resolved then and there that shivering in a cold shack at sixteen years of age was not how my life should end. I had more glorious adventures to experience than dying, and my visit by Miss Silverheels that afternoon was certainly glorious. Starting that minute, I would renew my life and again seek what riches the world had to offer. The first thing I wanted to do was to install a window in that dark cabin.

Miss Silverheels had the sad look again, "You will have to continue healing without me, Mr. Tom... Thomas Boone... I have a rash."

CHAPTER 9

Lancelot Slade

Old Tom

Within a few days I was well enough to remove the handkerchief from the door, leave the cabin, and walk about town. I first reported to duty at the Tabor Store. Mrs. Tabor and Baby Macksey had relocated to Denver but Mr. Tabor had remained behind to tend his store. He knew that Jake and I had gotten the pox. He knew about Jake's death and told me of thirty more: Big Al, Smilen George, Gold Dust, Anthony Sanders from the Livery and twenty more whose names I didn't know. Erik Svensson, the Swede who yelled "I'm a stayen" was the first to die. When I asked the condition of Miss Silverheels, he didn't know, because with Big Al's death, the Silver Slipper was closed. China Mary remained inside the saloon to care for Miss Silverheels but no one else was allowed inside or out.

The first thing I needed to do was to find my pack train and bring the animals home. Then I would find Miss Silverheels, thank her, and repay her kindness, if possible.

I went to the Wolves' Den to find Lancelot Slade. I was afraid, but I thought that if I was polite, he would give me my animals back for a fee. I entered the saloon alone sorely wishing that Jake were alive and at my side.

Slade was sitting at a table facing the door, playing cards. "Thank you for watching my burros, Mr. Slade," I said, "May I have them back now?"

He put down his cards, pulled a revolver out of his pocket and said, "Five are still for sale, Kid; I already sold a jack. Those burros can be bought for fifty dollars each. Do you have that kind of money?"

With bravery nourished only by my anger, I yelled, "Those are my burros! You have no right to them!"

"This gives me the right," and he pointed that revolver at my left eye. "I've been looking for a good excuse to shoot you for some time now."

I left scared and angry, but I left quickly nevertheless. For the time being, I could use Jake's horse Muffin, so I walked to the livery stable to get her. The sign **"Anthony Sander's Livery"** had been taken down and replaced with another sign.

Lancelot Slade
Dealer of Fine Horses, Mules, and Burros

No one was around but a bearded old man sitting on a chair with a scatter gun on his lap. "I came for my horse," I said.

"I need to see a bill of sale," he replied.

"You don't understand, I need to get Muffin, a chestnut mare. She belonged to my friend, Jake, and was being boarded here under Anthony Sander's care."

"Anthony Sander is dead. This is no longer a livery, it is a sale barn owned by Mr. Lancelot Slade. If you wish to purchase any of these fine animals, you need to deal with him."

I went back to Mr. Tabor's store. "Where do I find a Law Man?"

"No such person," he responded, "but if this is about your burros, you may find what you seek at the Claims Trade."

The Claims Trade was a small log building in the center of the town. It was run by a thin, spectacled, balding man named Thomas Saggons, perhaps the only man in town besides Richard with an education beyond grammar school. He bought and sold claims and had become the wealthiest man in Buckskin Joe. Whenever a meeting was called, such as the meeting to discuss the pox, it was Mr. Saggons who led the proceedings. We referred to him simply as "The Sage." Inside the office with him were eight angry men. I knew them all: Big Jake from Minnesota; Minnie McKeever, an Irishman who breaks out in song when drunk; Byron Woodyard, the claims recorder who sang nights at the Silver Slipper for tips; Percival Coty, the assayer; Scotty Browne, a skinny miner from Scotland who worked hard and drank hard; and three prospectors who were on my daily route up Buckskin Gulch, Rocken Rob and the Weidmeyer brothers. Most had red pox scars like mine, had trusted horses to Anthony Sanders at his livery, and had lost those animals to Lancelot Slade when he took over ownership. Each man carried a grudge such as mine. Slade had claimed ownership of all the animals at the livery upon Anthony's death because of what he said was an unpaid gambling debt. Most horses in the stable were returned to their rightful owners for a two dollar "Transfer of ownership" fee. Eight horses, including Muffin, were not returned because the owners had died of the Pox;

and twelve horses, as well as my six burros, were not returned out of spite for those of us who had protected Miss Silverheels from Lancelot Slade those few weeks ago. Mr. Slade was determined to punish us for violating the "law of the pack." He surely would protect that "law" with his fellow "wolves."

Byron the singer who had remained mostly quiet until this point practically yelled, "There's three things that earn a man a necktie party: Stealen a horse, jumpen a claim, or insulten a woman and Slade's done all three. I say we hang him!"

There were shouts of approval but the Sage held up both arms to quiet us and said, "We can act like civilized men." He told us of a law in Illinois whereby citizens, in the absence of a marshal, could arrest a person who had committed a crime and take him to a court for justice, and we all felt that Lancelot Slade had committed numerous crimes including the theft of our animals. There was such a court in Denver and it was agreed that we would go as a group to the Wolves' Den, demand our property back, or arrest Lancelot for horse thievery and take him immediately to a Denver jail. There were nine of us standing there, all angry at the bold injustice of having our animals taken in an act of apparent revenge. We all were worried about what reaction Slade's friends would have, but we thought that we would have the safety of numbers if we acted quickly and secretly.

Knowing that everyone was possibly as afraid of Slade as I was, the Sage quoted a line from Shakespeare: "A coward dies a thousand deaths, the valiant dies but one."

Rocken Rob whose face was red with anger yelled, "Forget being valiant or dying, I say we shoot him first; then take him to Denver for a trial!"

I held up my hand and uttered the only words I said at that meeting, "Killing Slade would make us be the bigger sinners." And some in the group nodded.

As agreed to at the meeting, we met at noon the following day at the assayer's office to make our arrest. I had never been more afraid in my life, for I feared Lancelot Slade more than any person I had ever known. By now the number of angry men had grown to twelve, and we walked to the Wolves Den like a small army. Though our army of a dozen was marching to encounter just one man, I was shaking with fear. My chest certainly was not puffed out. I just wanted my burros and Jake's horse, Muffin, back. Each of us had a weapon, mine being my scatter gun. Lancelot was standing alone outside the saloon when we approached. We stopped when we came within ten feet of him. Though we all assumed the Sage to be our leader, we had not elected a person to do our speaking and we stood silently for about half a minute. I was shaking. Finally the Sage said, "We came for our horses."

Lancelot Slade did the same thing he did to me the day before, pointed that revolver at the Sage's eyes and said, "Five hundred dollars for each horse," and looking at me with a fierce look in his eyes, he said, "Those burros now cost you two hundred dollars each."

Again we were silent. In all these months alone on the frontier I had not successfully removed that yellow stripe from my back, and it was me who first lacked the courage to stand there. I quietly turned around to walk away. The other eleven followed suit. No one said a word as we moved down the street; we just slowly retreated, not even knowing our destination. Though I could not see him as I shuffled, I could sense Slade's gun pointed at my back.

When we were about twenty yards away we heard a gun shot. I turned around, saw the evil Slade still standing in front of the saloon with his pistol in his hand, and I fired my shot gun at him. The others had also turned and fired what weapons they had in unison. Slade had a look of surprise on his face and crumpled to the ground. Though no one reloaded, we all kept our weapons aimed at him.

Father Dyer was in town and came running to the sound of the gun fire. He walked up to the now lifeless and bloody body, knelt over it, and began praying. We put down our weapons and took off our hats as he prayed. When he finished, he replaced his own cap and glared at us with anger. In his booming preacher's voice he roared as if speaking to multitudes, "The wages of sin is death," and then walked away.

We stood there in silence for awhile till Byron, the singer, asked, "What does that mean?" Everyone shrugged but I said, "My grandfather used to say that to those he thought were sinners... It comes from the Bible. Father Dyer has just told us that we are not going to heaven."

"And be with the likes o' him, a yellen all the time?" questioned Minnie McKeever, the Irishman.

"He shot first!" yelled the Scotsman named Browne, "We had to shoot him, didn't we?"

We didn't know the answer to that question, but we knew that we had to do something with his body. No one wanted to touch that bloody corpse so we tied ropes around his ankles and dragged him away leaving a pink trail in the snow.

Word spread quickly and by the time we approached the cemetery a small crowd had developed, and most in it were applauding. I did not feel pride; I felt shame, for as we were tying him up, The Sage picked up Lancelot's revolver.

"Why, this gun is cold as a witch's heart!"

We may never know who fired that first shot, but with that cold pistol, it certainly was not Lancelot Slade; he had not fired a single bullet.

We apparently had just executed a man; not necessarily an innocent one, but no matter how evil, he was still one of God's children. I had just participated in breaking that one commandment that I had always believed would be the easiest of the ten to keep — "Thou shalt not kill."

Some thought it might have been a blast of gunpowder from the Phillips load that started all that shooting. Many remained unconvinced that Slade had not somehow fired at us while we were walking away. One witness said the first shot came from an open window at The Silver Slipper, for he saw black smoke rolling out of it right after the commotion. China Mary was at the Tabor Store at the time, Big Al was dead, and only Miss Silverheels was inside the saloon. We all knew that, though she may have held a grudge against Lancelot, she was very sick. I told the group that a woman that dainty and flawless would never shoot a gun, even when in good health. They all nodded, though I remain certain that some wondered if she somehow had protected us from being shot in the back. I sometimes still wonder myself.

The prospector who called himself Rocken Rob looked in the dead man's pockets to retrieve a time piece that Lancelot had unfairly won from him, but all he found were four dirty silver dollars. With those coins we paid the two black grave diggers a dollar each to bury him in that cold frozen earth, gave Father Dyer a dollar to hold a small service and pray for his soul, and paid Dean Sherman, the leather and wood worker a dollar to make a marker. Though not a fancy tomb stone like the ones back home, it was a nice wooden marker, white washed and burned with this inscription on its face:

Lancelot Slade
Died November 30, 1861
The Wages of Sin is Death

December 2, 1862

Dear Mr. and Mrs. Lewis,

I am sad to inform you that Jake passed away on this November 22, 1861 from a disease we call "the pox."

As we have only recently gotten a postal office, I know that Jake had never written a letter to you so I shall fill in what has transpired for the past few months.

After traveling across the great American Desert, we walked another hundred miles deep into the mountains, and made it to the gold country by the middle of June and settled into a booming community called Buckskin Joe.

Jake lived a clean life, attended church services with me, and worked hard. We did not find the riches in gold we came for but found moderate success in our endeavors. He had become a respected carpenter, but his dream was to build and run a boarding house here once spring arrived. His valor was unquestioned and he was quick to respond to other's plights, including saving Martha and Mason from being resold into slavery.

I, too, got the pox, but am recovering as I write this letter. I do not know why some die and some live, nor do I know why God chose Jake to go and me to stay, but I do know that I miss him.

When we got sick, Jake and I wrote our last wishes. His wish was for you to have the money he was saving to build the boarding house and I will give it to you when I return to Grass Creek this spring. I will then also share stories of his kindness, bravery, and friendship.

We buried your son, and my friend, on a sunny November morning on a hill overlooking the town. Reverend John Dyer, the traveling Methodist minister, delivered a service for Jake and there were many in attendance as everyone liked Jake for his warm smile and kind words.

I made a marker from a wide pine board, white-washed it, borrowed some words from the book of Matthew, and burned this inscription along with a cross onto the sturdy plank with a hot iron:

Jacob Lewis
1843-1861
Well done, thou good and faithful friend.

Sincerely,

Thomas Boone

CHAPTER 10

Miss Silverheels

Wednesday, December 4, 1861

It is good to be writing again. I have not written in my journal for nearly a month, and so much has happened. I am feeling well but weary. I do not feel like writing about what has transpired in the last few weeks, but I shall write a short summary lest I ever forget: Jake and I got small pox, my burros got stolen, Miss Silverheels nursed us, Jake died, Miss Silverheels and I share a secret, twelve of us killed Lancelot Slade, I got my burros back with the exception of Abel.

Should I never write another word again or lose this journal, I think that I shall never forget a minute of those tragic last days of November, 1861.

I will write today only about retrieving the burros. As a group, those of us who were involved in the shooting of Lancelot Slade walked straight for the livery where our stolen animals were for sale.

The sign read

Lancelot Slade
Dealer of Fine Horses, Mules, and Burros

but the man was dead and we wanted our property back. The old man guarding the livery ran away as soon as he saw the dead body being dragged to the cemetery. We felt as if this livery had no owner as Anthony Sanders had died of the pox and Lancelot Slade's body was freezing at the cemetery. All we had to do was to walk in and greet our animals. I found five of the burros outside in the pen and gave them some hay and oats. They were all very hungry. Abel was missing. Slade seemingly has indeed sold him to some unknown miner. I found Muffin, fed her as well, then saddled her, for I needed to find Abel and get him back.

I rode for the rest of the day until I was exhausted for I am still very weak, but found neither Abel nor any word on his disappearance. I shall resume my search tomorrow.

Thursday, December 5, 1861

I have now given up the hunt for Abel for I have searched every gulch and settlement for miles and no one has seen a burro wandering or a prospector leading one. Abel is surely no longer in this area. I feel sad and guilty for allowing such a thing to happen. I do not wish to write any more about it.

Friday, December 6, 1861

I check daily at The Silver Slipper for any information on the condition of Miss Silverheels. Though the saloon is closed, China Mary always answers my knock, accepts my gifts of biscuits or broth, and always gives me the same answer. "Miss Silverheels is very, very poorly."

Other men are recuperating and telling tales similar to mine, though no one has shared a dancing story and I keep that last visit to me a secret. Upon seeing a red handkerchief on a door, Miss Silverheels and China Mary would enter to care for those inside, be it a shack containing just one man or a boarding house with twenty. China Mary would light fires and do heavy chores and Miss Silverheels would tend to the sick and dying. Altogether seventy of us have credited our lives to the beautiful dancing lady. Thirty of us did not survive. The account of a man dying of the pox is always the same. Miss Silverheels would pay the two black men a dollar each out of her own money to bury the victim in the nearby cemetery. She always wept.

I frequently stand outside the Silver Slipper in the snow waiting for word on her improvement, but it never comes. Other survivors often share my wait, but whether it be just me, or a dozen of us, we never hear anything but "Miss Silverheels is very, very poorly." Always the talk is of our angel. We find that no one even knows her name or where she comes from. Some suspect a long relationship with Big Al. Was she his wife? We doubt it, for Big Al and Miss Silverheels each lived in separate rooms and neither was ever seen visiting the other room. Is she his sister and recently widowed from her husband? It would certainly explain the black dress and veil, but she is so petite and lovely and Big Al was big and ugly. We settled on a speculation whereby she was widowed from one of Big Al's brothers, and lacking funds to return home, came to become employed as a dancer at The Silver Slipper. To date, no man has stepped forward to claim so much as even a quick kiss from our angel. I like this story of the stranded widow. I keep my secret and tell no one of the private show she gave me.

Saturday, December 7, 1861

Today a burly German drove a sturdy freighter into Buckskin Joe and stopped in front of the Silver Slipper. I recognized him as the driver that brought Miss Silverheels to town all those months ago. Four of us were standing vigil including the Sage when the German motioned us to his wagon. "I am Aloysius Beaumeister's brother, August, and am here to collect his possessions and to pay respects to the woman you know as Miss Silverheels." He showed us papers to prove his relationship. Though none of us knew Big Al's full name, the Sage looked them over and motioned him down.

"She is very ill," I said. He looked at me, nodded, locked the brakes on his freighter, and proceeded to the door, entering without even knocking.

The big German's face with its scraggly reddish orange beard looked almost animal like. "Surely if Miss Silverheels was the widow of a brother, she must not mind being with homely men." I whispered to the Sage. "This man's face reminds me of a dead buffalo I saw on the plains."

We stood there for twenty minutes until August came outside carrying a whiskey barrel. "Your Miss Silverheels is well, but weak, and shall be out and about by morning."

We cheered. I offered to help, but August declined the offer and carried keg after keg to the freighter. I went home determined to see Miss Silverheels in the morning and properly thank her for saving my life.

Tonight I heated a couple of buckets of water, and took a bath in a tub I have made out of a whisky barrel because I want to look good for Miss Silverheels. I then washed my clothes in the tub as well, and they are drying by the fire.

Sunday, December 8, 1861

Before dawn I awoke to the sound of commotion and went outside. It was still dark but the sky was orange with the glow of a nearby fire; the Silver Slipper was in flames. I grabbed a shovel and a bucket and without even buttoning my coat, ran down the street to help. Many a man had already arrived to the scene, but no one was even fighting the fire, for the Silver Slipper was completely engulfed by the inferno. All we could do was shovel snow on neighboring structures to prevent their incineration. Soon the whole town was at the fire, some helping, some watching, some not knowing what to do, but all of us standing there in that cold December air were obviously upset. The most respected of the drinking establishments was now dying a fiery death. Big Al's brother August, his mules, whiskey, and freighter were gone, and apparently Miss Silverheels had left with him for she was nowhere to be seen. By the time it was light out, the Silver Slipper had burned to a smoldering heap of embers, steaming in the now falling snow. I just stood there watching as did about fifty of us pock-scarred survivors of the recent plague.

"Now what?" someone asked. No one responded.

Monday, December 9, 1861

There is now so much snow on the ground that few are prospecting anymore. Buckskin Creek runs with only a trickle beneath the ice making the running of a sluice or panning almost impossible. I am still weak from the pox, so most of my strength is consumed in keeping warm. I use my idle time socializing with other pox victims. I do not own a mirror, so I have not seen how scarred my face must be, but if I look like the others, or if my face is as pock marked as my chest, I must look a fright.

Often the talk is of Miss Silverheels. Surely, she must look as wretched as the rest of us. While we think of her beauty as we remember it, we know that she can never be a dance hall girl again, as there is a certain disgust that many hold for people with pock-scarred faces, especially severely blemished women. Her only hope now of a comfortable life is to find and marry a man who could see beyond her pitted skin. Many of us here would gladly summon Father Dyer and marry her today no matter how disfigured she must be…me included. No, especially me!

The survivors have agreed to collect money as a gift to Miss Silverheels, so that she may live in comfort. I gave two dollars and some flakes of gold to start the fund and added two of Jake's dollars to reimburse his burial costs. A canvas bag at the Tabor Store will be used to collect donations.

Thursday, December 12, 1861

In just three days we have collected over two hundred dollars as a reward to Miss Silverheels for saving our town. Even those who were spared of the disease are contributing. Two hundred dollars is a year's income here for a working man and is enough to buy a modest home in Denver with wooden floors and glass windows. We advertised our appreciation as well as our generous reward in most newspapers including the large Rocky Mountain News in Denver. China Mary remains in his little shack by the creek and does not know or say where she is. I feel that Miss Silverheels is in the area and will claim her reward soon.

Saturday, February 15, 1862

It has now been three months since the plague. The canvas sack containing the reward money stopped growing at two hundred and forty-seven dollars plus nearly five ounces of gold dust. The reward remains unclaimed, and it now seems that Miss Silverheels has left the area with no intention of returning.

We held another town meeting today to determine the fate of the canvas bag and its contents. Some wanted to erect a statue, some wanted to re-build the Silver Slipper in her honor, but most have wearied of all the fuss, spent all reserve cash in this long, cold winter, and just want the money returned. It was I who yelled out, "Let's name that mountain in her honor!" and I pointed toward that great snow covered Mountain known by so many names. A roar of agreement arose through the crowd of two hundred. Unlike the way we unofficially name things at the newspaper, the Sage said that formally naming a mountain was as easy as filing a mining claim and he would take care of recording the name on Monday. From today on, that mountain which rises like a queen above the high plains grassland known now as the South Park will be known as Mount Silverheels.

Old Tom

No one ever learned the fate of Miss Silverheels, and eventually the money was returned. Some say she lingered as a hermit near the mining camp of Buckskin Joe, for a veiled woman was sometimes said to be placing flowers and sobbing near the graves of smallpox victims. Some assumed she either married or was taken care of by Big Al's brother August. Years later, I read of a Confederate nurse who tended to the wounded, no matter how unsafe the conditions, or how gruesome the wounds were. She was known as the "Veiled Canary" for it was said that she wore a veil and hummed or sang as she tended to the dying. Surely this was Miss Silverheels as taking care of others was what she did the best.

No matter what the truth may be, her story has grown to become one of the legends of the West, and her memory shall remain for as long as that great mountain rises above the plains. From whatever direction you approach the gold country around what once was Buckskin Joe, you must first cross that great twenty-five mile diameter grassland known as The South Park. Standing distinct among the other mountains, much like Pike's Peak dominates the eastern Colorado Plains, is Mount Silverheels. She seems to be saying: "Do not fear this awesome place; I will care for you."

CHAPTER 11

The Race

Monday, February 17, 1862

I have now lived in the town of Buckskin Joe for nine months. When Jake and I arrived on that cool June morning, we found a tent city of perhaps a thousand men and two or three women. Mr. Tabor was digging the foundation for his store which was to be the first structure in town with a pitched roof. Nearly all dwellings at that time were tents or makeshift houses made of canvas tents erected over a square layer or two of logs. Some men had built more permanent lodging out of logs or sawn boards, but they were small, crude affairs with a flat board or canvas roof.

Daily for the last three quarters of a year the air has been filled with the sounds of saws, axes, and hammers as humble dwelling after humble dwelling was erected. The small lonely shack that Jake and

I built is still my favorite building in town. While only about twelve feet by sixteen feet it became a cozy abode for us. Though it had no windows, paint, floor, or cupboards, it felt like home because we had built it ourselves. Like the Tabor store, we built it with a pitched roof and shingled it with pine boards. The loneliness is due to Jake's absence.

Jake built sixteen other dwellings before he died. I see each of them daily on my walks, and view them with both pride and sadness, for I miss Jake dearly.

Stores that once had been freight wagons with a canvas top are now housed in sturdy wooden structures with wood floors and windows. As of this date, there is no glass to put in these windows so light comes through the oiled deerskin or canvas that is nailed to the window openings. As soon as a shipment of glass arrives, we may see buildings with enough light to read by. I may add a window or two to my little house.

The Silver Slipper was the first building in town to have a whitewashed interior but now numerous businesses and even a few homes are white washed inside and out. No one has cleaned the site of the Silver Slipper, and the charred remains poke out of the snow as a constant reminder of the once happy place.

Caroline Coty got her wish to become a school teacher. There are eight children in town now, and they all attend school in a room at the assayer's office. She sent all the way to Denver for that keg of linseed oil and bag of iron oxide and that building now stands distinguished above all others in town by its pleasant rust red color.

Three thousand people now live in this town and more seem to arrive each day. Not all are coming here solely to find gold. Many are leaving their homes to avoid the war that is now raging in the East. Even today, most are men, but we have about one hundred women, as well as those eight school age children and a few tykes such as baby Emma and Macksey. About one half of the women came here with their husbands, and the other half are women who make a living by being a woman.

There are still about as many tents as wood buildings, but they are being replaced by warmer wooden structures for even in this cold February wind there is still that sound of saws, axes, and hammers. There often is also the sound of far-off steam engines and the pounding of stamp mills as ore is pulverized by those giant iron hammers. The Watts brothers' steam-powered sawmill can be heard humming in the distance as they saw timber for the mines and for new houses. Frequently you can hear the boom of gunpowder as rock is loosened in the Phillips lode about a mile away.

Soon this "boom town," as we call it, should be a thriving little city with painted buildings of all colors, and I shall be proud to call it my home.

Tuesday, February 18, 1862

Digging, panning, and pretty much every activity has all but stopped for the winter up above town, and I now make my trek just every other day up to Kite Lake and back. A twelve mile journey that used to take just a few hours now takes me all day as I struggle through the snow on my snow shoes. Whenever we come upon a snow drift, Eve stops and refuses to put one foot forward until I break a path for her. She proceeds cautiously while the rest of the team follows in her footsteps. What men remain up above town are hunkered down in their cabins waiting for a spring thaw as the snow is now several feet deep and Buckskin Creek is frozen solid. The men do not buy any goods other than a little food or grain, and I think that most men are conserving their money until the water again flows and panning for gold can resume. On those days when it is sunny and not blowing snow, I take the full train and some lumber for men to make repairs to their cabins, but mostly it is just me and Adam and Eve carrying a few bags of supplies.

Today was a pleasant and warm day. Out of boredom I loaded my burros and we walked downhill to see if I could peddle some goods to the men down by the river. There is a good wagon road down there and little need for burros so I did not expect to sell many goods, but anything is better than staying in this lonely cabin. Unlike the conditions above Buckskin Joe, there is not much snow down there, and a few men are still working their claims. I sold very little hardware or food, but did have some success selling Mr. Tabor's new shipment of condensed milk. Two miles below Buckskin Joe is a little settlement by the river with no permanent buildings, no stores and not even a name. With only one exception, the little town consists of just a few dozen tents with a few dozen miners shivering in the cold by an outdoor fire. The fire burning was one that Grizzly Hatch would call a "white man's fire" for it blazes far more than is necessary to keep a person warm. The twenty or so tents in this settlement form a canvas ring around this blaze and the men huddle at the flap of the tent to face its heat. Most of the tents have pine branches, pine needles and whatever else these men could find to add a blanket of warmth to their primitive quarters. Though there is no store in this little settlement, I sold very little in the way of goods to any of these men and I suspect that these men are low on money.

Close to the river, where water can still be found running beneath the ice, is a very large tent erected over a square of logs about four feet tall and the only business of any kind in this little community. A hand-painted sign in front proudly proclaims:

ALMA'S PLACE
HOT STEW AND COFFEE
10¢

As it was about noon, I entered Alma's Place, willing to pay this modest price for a warm meal. I almost never purchase a meal at one of these establishments, but the smell of hot food was too tempting to pass up. This spacious canvas building reminded me of some of the tents that accompanied circuses back in Missouri for it was tall enough to comfortably stand in and was heated by the cook fire burning under a huge cast iron kettle in one corner. It felt very pleasant inside, pleasant enough that I took my coat off. The place was large enough to have a table with ten chairs. Six bearded men were sitting at the table when I entered and I sat down in one of the four remaining seats. Without saying a word, a hardy woman of about thirty five years, whom I guess to be Alma, ladled a steaming bowl of stew, poured a tin cup of hot coffee and placed them in front of me.

"One thin dime, no tokens, no Confederate."

The stew, while not as good as Mother's, was quite tasty and had potatoes, carrots, and onions, as well as generous quantities of shredded meat, probably buffalo or elk. The coffee was better than any I have tasted in nearly a year with no hint of parched corn to make it cheaper as is the common practice here. I resolved then and there that Alma's Place will be a noontime destination, on occasion, from here on out, as a dime is fair price for food that would cost me nearly that much to make.

As I was finishing my cup of coffee, a skinny young man about my age entered and sat down next to me. "Are those your burros outside?"

I nodded. "Fine lookin' animals," he said. "Mine are outside as well."

He had his dime ready before Alma served him and sat silently drinking his coffee for a minute. "I run the route from Park City up to London Mountain," he said. "You're not here to compete with me are you?"

I shook my head and assured him that I worked for The Tabor Store in Buckskin Joe, and my route goes from there, up to Kite Lake. "I'm only here today because the creek is frozen and I thought perhaps I could peddle some of Mr. Tabor's condensed milk down here by the river." He had come downhill from Park City for similar reasons and was trying to sell jarred peaches. As I had not eaten a peach in nearly a year and he had never even heard of canned milk, we made a trade of two cans of sweetened milk for two jars of delicious peaches and we shared a jar of peaches with milk on the spot. Alma did not seem to care.

Since Jake's passing I have had no one my own age to talk to. Will is not only my same age, but he runs a burro train as well, and we had a lot in common to talk about. We liked each other and agreed to meet at Alma's place for lunch three times a week throughout the remainder of this miserably cold winter.

Saturday, February 22, 1862

I have been meeting Will at Alma's Place every other day for a week now and look forward to a hot lunch and conversation. I did not know that anyone so similar to me lived in these mountains. He too had no horse to ride and walked here from near Chicago with five donkeys; and just like I do, he now refers to these animals as burros and has given them names: Flapjack, Biscuit, Cornpone, Ham and Egg.

Will is only a few months older than me and just as thin and young-looking. Like me, he is trying to grow a beard to cover pox scars on his face, but just like my beard, his looks more like the fuzz on one of those peaches than a stately growth of hair.

Sunday, February 23, 1862

Holly is my best friend. She follows me all day long on my route and sits quietly as I talk to the miners and do my trading. Before Jake died, she stayed outside our cabin with the burros and slept in a little house I built for her. Since Jake's death, I have had no one to talk to but her once I get home, so she stays inside with me. I read passages from books to her, and she just stares at me as if she understands. When I am excited about something, she gets excited and turns round and around in a happy circle on the floor. When I am sad, she seems to know and puts her head on my knee as I sit in my chair. She likes to be petted between her ears. Some people would be appalled at the idea of a dog inside a house, but I like having her with me.

I have come to believe that I do not see myself and my burros as others see us. I have known for months that most view me as I look and not how I feel. They call me "Kid," for to them I must seem quite young as I cannot grow a beard and I am still quite thin. I look at my burros, not as friends, as I do Holly, but as beasts of burden to help me secure the funds for that store in Grass Creek. Even though there is considerable snow on the ground, I still traverse five to nine miles uphill most mornings and the same five to nine downhill most afternoons. As we walk, we easily pass horses challenging the same route. Wagons drawn by horses, mules, or oxen do not even attempt the paths we easily walk. Almost daily I am asked to sell one of my burros, and always I refuse the request for I need these animals to earn money. What these men must see with envy is a spry lad leading five faithful and agile companions. I have walked perhaps three thousand miles at the side of these animals and while I perceive only work, these men surely see something different. Perhaps in this cold and lonely country, every lonesome man needs a companion. Perhaps a faithful burro could provide this need. Missouri has thousands of donkeys, and no one truly appreciates them there. It seems a shame that this imbalance exists.

There have been prophets such as Joseph in the Bible who could foresee the future. I do not profess to hold that ability, but I see a need in this area for countless more of these agile creatures. I can vision many a prospector walking up and down the sloping mountainsides with a trusty burro at his side carrying his gear. I also see lonely men with a need for a best friend. I think a burro could fill that purpose just as Salvador's old companion, Orito, does. Were it not for Holly, I may have died of loneliness months ago.

I sometimes wonder if I should travel home to Missouri and buy perhaps twenty of these loyal creatures, make a pack saddle for each, and return to this area to sell them for a profit. They could also carry merchandise for me to peddle that cannot be found here: warm stockings, wool hats, dried fruit and nuts. I can find all these goods, including the donkeys, right near Grass Creek. I have made a lot of money here, but I intend to get even richer, and this may be a good plan. This time I could ride Muffin instead of walking and take the easier Platte River route. That river begins only two miles from here and I can follow it all the way to the Missouri River without ever being more than a few yards from water.

I need to think on this plan.

Wednesday, February 25, 1862

Monday started out to be another pleasant and sunny day, but as I neared Alma's Place, the clouds darkened, and I could tell that we were in for yet another blizzard. It began blowing snow as I tied my train under some trees by the river. Will's train was already tied under other nearby trees, and I went in to Alma's for some warm food and coffee before I trudged back to my cabin in this now rapidly falling snow. Only a handful of men were inside, including Richard Hamilton who had ridden here to sell some of his newspapers. I sat with Richard and Will, and our discussion was mostly about the blizzard developing outside, guessing how long it would last or how deep the snow would be. When the last of our coffee was drunk, Alma suggested that we wait out the storm with free coffee. After pouring us some from a newly brewed pot, she brought over a clear glass bottle filled with a transparent liquid and uncorked it. Immediately I could smell the very sweet and distinct smell of mint. "The coffee is free, but the Peppermint will cost you five cents; no tokens, no Confederate."

There is very little candy to be found here in the mountains and I had not smelled or tasted peppermint in over a year. I gladly put a

172

five cent piece on the table. Richard and Will also presented coins and Alma poured some of the sweet smelling fluid in each of our steaming mugs of coffee.

I had a can of milk in my coat pocket, opened it with a knife, and added it to our drinks as well. None of us had ever tasted such a good beverage, and we emptied our mugs in minutes. "Here, Alma, is fifteen cents, we'll each have another," I generously offered and we each eagerly drank another cup. Richard soon came up with a dime and a half for another round and then Will produced another fifteen cents for three more mugs of the delicious brew. None of us, or at least not I, knew that what we were drinking was whiskey flavored with peppermint leaves, and I was unaware that the three of us were falling under the power of what Father Dyer calls "the devil's evil elixir." The conversation got fun with a lot of boasting from Will, and then me, about our burros and how fast we could travel in these mountains. Richard could sense a good competition and suggested that we hold a foot race alongside our best animals. We all had consumed too much of those spirits, and while I am not one to normally place bets, I agreed to the challenge. It reminded me of the competitions that Jake and I used to hold back in Grass Creek. Our wager was that the loser of a six mile foot race alongside our favorite burro would buy the winner a bowl of stew and a mug of peppermint coffee. We agreed to a three mile run from Buckskin Joe to Park City by way of a direct path through the steep hills. Then each of us will fill our panniers with ore from the creek and then race along the river another three miles to a finish line at Alma's place.

Richard asked if we minded if he advertised the race in his newspaper as a way to generate funds to buy wooden crosses for some of the unmarked graves in Buckskin Cemetery. Again the peppermint talked and we not only agreed, we were happy for the honor of getting our names in the printed word.

This all happened two days ago, and I am still ashamed of what went on at Alma's Place. Not only did I break a vow to never drink again, I got drunk, loud, and boastful, and attended outdoor church on Sunday with a very severe headache.

Richard, indeed, wrote of our upcoming race, and I read it this morning with great embarrassment. Now I have to run a silly foot race with a loaded burro while the whole town watches. If I lose this challenge, I will have cause for even more embarrassment. When I used to race Jake, he could easily outrun me in any competition, and I wonder if perhaps I am just a slow runner. My only advantage might be that I have learned that my burros will pull me along if I wrap the lead rope behind my back. Number Four is my strongest animal and when I use her to carry loads, she frequently pulls me along making it easy to move at a faster pace with little effort. I will use Number Four and let her pull me along at a fast clip. I'm sure that Will does not know this trick.

I shall never put peppermint in my coffee again.

Thursday, February 27, 1862

This evening after a full day of work, we had our contest. I still am amazed at what people will do here for entertainment as about two dozen men and one woman arrived to watch the competition. The contest advertised in the newspaper had produced enough interest to sell over three hundred wagers at five cents each. Whichever entry had the guess of the winning time closest to Richard's official time will receive one half of the takings.

I, of course, chose Number Four to be my running companion, and Will was with his favorite jenny, Egg. Each animal had on a pack saddle that we had made while back on the farm, and each saddle had a shovel and two empty panniers hanging from the tree.

Among those on hand to watch the start of the event were two carpenters named Coulter and Long, a new dance hall girl named Cynthia, the Sage, that skinny Scotsman named Scotty Browne, and Richard.

174

Scotty brought a bottle of whiskey to keep him company as he watched. I was not surprised to see him as he seems to be anywhere that he knows a lively affair will happen. On about every evening you can hear his voice stand out from the others from the inside of a saloon having a good time, yet in the morning he is among the first to swing a pick at his claim. He frequently holds one finger up in the air as if about to give wise advice, and then says, "Whiskey can get you through times o' nae money better than money can get you through times o' nae whiskey."

He brought Cynthia, a short but buxom dance hall girl from the Double Bar J Saloon. She introduced herself to me by saying, "My name is Cynthia, but you can just call me Sin." I have heard that miners line up for the opportunity to pay her fee of ten cents a dance, and I suspect that most of these men are curious to find what area of "Sin" she is talking about. Scotty says that most men just want an opportunity to dance close to what's behind that revealing black dress. I, myself, felt uncomfortable just looking at her in that daring black costume, and I do not think that I would ever get the courage to dance with her or any other dance hall girl for that matter, but I will have to say that she is a quite striking young woman.

Richard was wearing his black coat and that tall beaver hat and looked very official; he even carried a black walking stick and had a monocle in his right eye. The Sage, also wearing a black stove pipe hat, scratched a line in the path with his boot, and Will and I stood side by side behind that line with our burros. Number Four seemed to sense the excitement and was pulling at my rope to get started. I had already wrapped her lead rope around my back when I noticed Will doing the same thing. Seeing that Will had learned this trick, as well, my best hope was that Number Four was the better burro. Scotty stood in front of us and held that index finger wisely up in the air, but before he could say a word, Cynthia reached inside that black dancing dress where it was cut so low, produced a very tiny pistol, and shot it into the air to start the race. Number 4 bolted and pulled me along and we led for the first mile or so, but rarely by more than a few dozen paces. As we started to climb a fairly steep, though small hill on the path, I started to tire and slowed Number Four to a walk. Will and Egg easily passed us and continued with a slow, but steady canter. By the time I reached Mosquito Creek, Will already had his panniers filled with gravel and was tying them on Egg's saddle. I had regained some energy by then, filled my panniers, tied them to the pack saddle and began running towards Alma's place. Number Four could tell we were heading in a homeward direction and began pulling me as we ran but by then we were nearly ten minutes behind. I could see Will and Egg walking up to that very large tent when I was still about a half mile away so I gave up my run and continued the distance at a walk.

Will had won fairly and I humbly congratulated him. He had beaten me soundly, but I didn't much care for his gloating. There were about twenty people including Scotty, Sin, and the two carpenters crowded in Alma's Place drinking peppermint coffee and listening to Will crow about his superior skills. I smiled and listened in silence with only a mug of cold water in my hand as he claimed that he won due to superior abilities honed on the plains outside of Chicago, but I am certain that I lost because I am not completely recovered from the pox.

I guess that I must buy him that mug of stew but I will not drink the peppermint coffee.

THE BUCKSKIN PRESS
February 28, 1862

This Friday past, two members of our community held a footrace with trusty burros by their sides to see which young man is the true master of the "Rocky Mountain Canary." William Reeves, whose train supplies miners from the Park City Mercantile, ran alongside his trusty burro, Egg. and easily outdistanced our own Thomas Boone of the Tabor Store and his burro Number Four. Mr. Reeves completed the six mile course in 47 minutes and 57 seconds to Mr. Boone's 56 minutes.

A lottery was held to guess the winning time of the race and it was won by our own Scotty Brown who promptly used his winnings to buy spirits for those in attendance. Fifteen dollars was raised by the lottery and will be used to purchase wooden crosses for fifteen unmarked graves of pox victims.

We at the Buckskin Press are proud to see such enthusiasm shown in the depths of this bitter winter by two of our younger members of the community.

- Richard Hamilton-Editor

CHAPTER 12

A Time to Go Home

Friday, February 28, 1862

Today as I was walking by Mr. Dodge's postal office I heard him yelling to me that I had received a letter. Some men here get a letter or card every week, or so, but this is my first. It was written over two months ago but it just got here this morning. I now have a piece of paper with actual words written by someone back home. I keep it in my pocket and read and reread it about once every hour. It's from Becky.

I thought that by now she would have forgotten all about me, but it was a good letter. She even hinted at a future together. I will not write much tonight, I think that I will just read her words a few more times....

Dearest Tom,

Receiving not one but two letters from you has been such a thrill for me! I sure do miss our Sunday walks home, life here just isn't quite the same without you. How I long to hear about the adventures you are experiencing! I am quite envious, as the daily habits in Grass Creek keep me busy, but honestly half the time I feel bored to tears!

I am so happy to hear that Holly has been such a blessing to have around. Just thinking of her warm tongue and coffee colored coat makes me smile. I am happy I was able to provide some gift for you to remember me by. When you return in July, I imagine she'll be so big and well trained that I won't even recognize her. You and Holly will have learned so much on your travels, and all I've done is the usual chores. Hopefully I will have at least one exciting tale to share with you by the time you've returned!

Our barn cat had five sweet little kittens just a few weeks back. They are already getting big and constantly rough-housing. I love to sit in the hay and let them climb all over me. They have brand new baby whiskers and breath that smells sweet and warm like milk. They are a nice distraction and I spend as much of my time as I'm allowed to with them.

Mother and I have been quite fearful of the men who have been raiding and burning farms. Father and my brothers assure us that they will keep us safe, but the violence seems to be coming closer and closer. I pray that our families will be kept safe and that these attacks will soon pass. I also pray that my brothers will not choose to fight in this war, but I fear for the worst.

Mother and I stopped by your home the other day with some cookies that we made and everyone seemed happy and well, although I imagine they miss you dearly.

I think of you every night before I fall asleep, and wonder what you're thinking about, if you're even awake that *is. I imagine you're thinking about gold and riches and the possibilities the future has for you; I only hope I might be a part of that. When you return come July, I shall be so glad to see you and Holly and hear your stories.*

Christmas Day is just a week away and I hope that you will have a blessed day and good friends to share it with.

With Warm Affections
Becky

Friday, February 28, 1862 (four hours later)

"Good friends to share it with." I was alone all day.

Saturday, March 1, 1862

Another blizzard arrived today bringing perhaps a foot of snow this time. How long can a winter last? On a pleasant March morning in Missouri there are signs that spring is about to arrive: buds are forming on the trees, birds are beginning to return from a winter's absence, daffodils planted on the south side of the house are poking up through the thawing ground. All we get here is more snow, cold and wind. Paths through the snow sometimes contain walls taller than my head and they get taller with each passing snowstorm. Those who were here last year say that the leaves do not return on the trees until the middle of June. I would love a life in Buckskin Joe if the summer weather remained year round. I would love a life in Buckskin Joe if I didn't shiver much of the year.

We always had four seasons where I grew up: Spring, Summer, Fall and Winter. Here in these mountains we have four seasons just like the rest of the world but they are named differently: June, July, August and Winter.

I would fancy it here and could survive these harsh winters, if I just made close friends like I had back home. I miss Jake; I miss my family; I miss Becky.

Tonight as I was walking home alone in the early darkness, I heard Minnie McKeever, the Irishman playing his fiddle and singing in his deep baritone voice. I stopped and listened to the sad lyrics of his song:

> *"Mid pleasures and palaces,*
> *Though I may roam,*
> *Be it ever so humble,*
> *There's no place like home;*
> *Home, home sweet, sweet home!*
> *There's no place like home!"*

I cannot get those lyrics out of my head. Though Buckskin Gulch is the most beautiful place I have ever seen and perhaps one of the most beautiful spots on this great earth, I just cannot feel at home here in the winter. When the weather was warm and Jake was alive, I felt as if this humble cabin were a palace on a hill. We often left the door open to allow light to beam in through its south face. The cabin was pleasantly warm and bright. The trickle of Buckskin Creek sang to us as its waters began a thousand mile adventure to the sea. Only the braying of a burro disturbed the solitude as we sat on the porch and read, or wrote, or made music. After a long day at work we would sit in front of our cabin and bask in the last rays of the sun until it lowered itself over the canyon walls. Life was good.

Now because the sun is so low in the sky, it is late morning before that orange ball rises above the mountains to the southeast and by mid-afternoon, scarcely five hours later, it hides itself behind the mountains to the southwest. I walk home to a lonely, dark cabin, build a fire and wait perhaps an hour and a half before the place is warm enough to remove my coat. Snow that I track in on my boots remains frozen on the floor in front of that drafty door. It remains there all night and all the next day until I pack it down with another layer upon my return. Holly still sleeps inside the cabin. Once the sun goes down, she and the cold are my only companions.

Men who used to stop by just to read newspapers pasted to the wall no longer stop by for fear of catching the pox. I have never considered myself to be a lonely person, but I am now a forlorn and solitary soul.

I relieve the solitude somewhat by reading or by dealing myself a lonely hand of Jake's cards. I can sit in the light of my oil lantern and escape boredom for hours. I get excited when I am learning new things, but when I finish a book or newspaper or successfully arrange a deck of cards, I look around my dark cabin and all I see is loneliness, and my mind goes back to those lyrics:

> *"I gaze on the moon*
> *As I tread the drear wild,*
> *And feel that my mother*
> *Now thinks of her child;*
> *Home, home sweet, sweet home!*
> *There's no place like home!"*

Sometimes my mind wanders back to that day when Miss Silverheels danced for me in front of the fire and that vision turns to dreaming of Becky. I think of her often. I would not be lonely if Becky were around. I wonder if she misses me. I wonder if she knows how to dance.

> *"An exile from home,*
> *Splendor dazzles in vain,*
> *Oh, give me my lowly*
> *Thatched cottage again;*
> *Home, home sweet, sweet home!*
> *There's no place like home!"*

For sixteen years Missouri was my home. For sixteen years I did not have to worry about freezing to death in the snow and cold. For most of those sixteen years, Becky lived a half mile away, not a thousand. I like this place we now call Colorado, I would like to think of it as home someday, but it is time to visit Missouri. Its time to make another trek, one not farther west for adventure, but east to find that peace of mind; to find warmth; to find Becky.

Sunday, March 2, 1862

Today is my seventeenth birthday, and I have no one to share it with, for in the midst of thousands of fortune seekers I am all alone. I still grieve for Jake, Miss Silverheels, and even Abel, though he was the most cantankerous ass I have ever been around. I have had enough misery to last a life time.

A year ago I believed that I could scoop up a fortune of yellow rock with almost no effort and I imagined myself riding back home in a king's coach. I do not believe that I will ever strike it rich, but I still dream of riding home with the pride of a successful adventure. I did make more money than I could possibly have earned back home, but it came mostly from hard labor and the hard work of the burros I had once scoffed. This long, cold winter has crushed my will to stay here another day. I want to go home, and I want to go home now!

I thought about this all last night. While my wish is to go home to Missouri, I think it will be for just a short visit, and I will return back to these mountains in time for summer. I enjoy adventure. I take pleasure in the sunshine and blue skies here. I just do not like the cold and misery and loneliness that a winter in this high country presents. If only Jake were alive; he could build a snug house down by the river where conditions are not quite so severe, but it is now time to start thinking about my return to where I came from. I am uncertain what I shall find there. I hear there is fighting all over the state as both the Union and the Confederacy wish to claim Missouri's allegiance. Bands of men called "Bushwackers" raid farms and towns, striking terror in the people. I do not wish to join in any dispute; I only want to go home. I miss Mother, Father, Michael, and friends; I miss the comfort of a more civilized place; I promised to return Jake's money to his parents, but most of all I wish to see Becky.

Though I have not become wealthy, the three hundred dollars I have saved is nearly enough to buy that wagon load of hardware I once dreamed of to start a store in Grass Creek, but I now understand that shop-keeping is not in my blood. I think clear and happy thoughts when I am traveling, but my feelings turn to gloom when I am trapped in this cold cabin as a blizzard howls outside. It has now become time to think about my future, and not only what I want to do but where I want to live. Perhaps a need to travel is what runs through my veins instead of a need to get rich. I think that my best plan is to go back to Missouri, use my limited money to buy about twenty donkeys, and load them with goods. I can be back to Colorado by summer when the weather is quite pleasant and the mountains and streams bustle with activity. This time, though, I shall not winter out in the high country, I will return as soon as I have sold all the burros and the goods they carried. I can be snuggled up to a warm Missouri fire with another jar of money by the time the snows fly. If my plans hold true, Becky might just be sitting by that warm fire and perhaps even be snuggled up next to me.

For safety this time I will not travel those dusty trails alone, nor will I walk. I cannot yet afford a good mule and wagon, but I have Muffin to ride and I can now afford the twenty-five dollars to join one of those outfits. Holly, of course, will be going back to Missouri as well. Mr. Tabor is soon sending one of his wagons to St. Louis for supplies and I know that he sends his wagons with an outfit out of Denver. I wonder if I can book passage on that wagon for some of my food and supplies while I ride Muffin.

Though they have been loyal animals and I am very fond of them, I will sell my burros as soon as I can find willing buyers who will not abuse them. While a donkey back east can be bought for a dollar or less, I have been offered up to twenty-five dollars here for one of my animals. Until today, I have always refused those offers, but I can certainly now use the money to travel for my next adventure.

Monday, March 3, 1862

When I announced my decision to go west, Father scorned the idea and said that I would "See the Elephant," and come back home hungry and defeated. He saw this elephant that symbolizes the West as a ferocious beast with large red eyes. There is another elephant story going around here that I like:

It seems that a farmer back east heard that a circus was coming to a neighboring town. The farmer had never seen an elephant so he decided to travel to the town to witness the parade with those circus elephants pulling the wagons. When he arrived at the town, riding on his buggy, the parade had already started and in the farmer's hurry he drove his horses almost head-over-heels into an elephant. His horse had never seen an elephant, either, and bolted causing his buggy to overturn, completely destroying it and breaking the man's arm.

When friends expressed sympathy for his losses, the farmer would simply reply, "I don't give a hank. I have seen the elephant."

I like this version. I may have "seen the elephant," but "I don't give a hank," either. I intend to see this magnificent giant again and again and again.

THE BUCKSKIN PRESS
March 4, 1862

An auction will be held this Saturday coming, at the Buckskin Livery, for the purpose of selling five healthy burros along with their pack saddles. The current owner, Thomas Boone, wishes to travel home to his native Missouri and will sell each burro to the highest bidder. Only cash transactions will be honored.

Tuesday, March 4, 1862, one week before departure

As I sit here in my cabin tonight I find myself very eager for my upcoming return home. I have been reflecting on how much I have changed in only one year. Last March if someone had asked me what my values were, I would have immediately responded that the Ten Commandments and the New Testament command to "love one another" were the only values I had and the only values I needed, and I would have believed myself.

It is time that I think about the questions: "Who am I, and who do I want to be?" I have watched for nearly a year now as men from both the Union and the Confederacy march off to war with God on their side, and I cannot see how God can be on either side when it comes to killing each other. I have watched the persecution of Negroes and Indians be defended with phrases from the Bible, often taken out of context, and I have seen greed at the expense of these beautiful mountains be justified with the quotation: "God planted that gold in these mountains and it is up to us to reap his bounty." In just one summer, most trees and other vegetation have disappeared along Buckskin Creek as well as in most other creeks and gulches in the area.

In Jake I learned the value of a good friend, and I hereby resolve to make many new friends. I will start with Will and Scotty. The loneliness that I now suffer in this cabin has caused me to understand that many of the men who frequent the saloons in town are perhaps just trying to relieve their own solitude and should not be judged as harshly as I once judged them. I always let Jake be the social one as he frequently did the talking for both of us. It is now time for me to become more approachable.

As I travel home in the near future, I will take my Bible with me, read it often, and try to follow all of the commandments and teachings, but I think that if I just make a commandment for myself to "be a good friend to all," then the other commandments and teachings might just fall in place with little effort. Perhaps the New Testament commandment to "Love one another" means just that, but with this war going on in the East and the greed going on here in the West, it seems that few men are heeding this instruction.

Thursday, March 6, 1862, five days until departure

The auction was held today at the livery. The Sage offered to be the auctioneer for no fee, and it went very well. I made one hundred and twenty-five dollars. About twenty men showed up to bid on my animals and another twenty showed just to have something to do on a bleak and windy March morning. Scotty was there with his whiskey bottle and was sharing its contents with his friends.

The Sage stood up and yelled, "Quiet!" But before he could say another word, a newcomer named Edward Snell yelled, "fifteen dollars each for all five including their saddles!"

Those in the crowd booed and yelled "One at a time...one at a time!" Scotty held up that familiar finger but said nothing.

The Sage then began the bidding for Eve at fifteen dollars and Edward yelled "I'm in." Big Jake yelled, "Sixteen" followed by a quick "Twenty-five" from Edward, and the bidding was over. Burro after burro was sold in almost exactly the same manner. As Adam, Number 3, Number 4, and Cain were brought out, the bidding started at fifteen dollars and ended with a bid for twenty-five from that newcomer, Edward Snell. Mr. Tabor was at the auction, as well, and tried to sell Mr. Snell my old route for ten dollars, but Edward was far too wise to fall for that one. In the end, he negotiated my old route from Mr. Tabor for no money at all, but rather a fifteen percent share of all sales. As I only got ten percent, he should be able to recoup his money rather quickly. He should do well here in my place as he is likely a better salesman than I, and I wish him well.

I fared better with Mr. Snell than Mr. Tabor did. I went up to Edward and asked if he had a place to live. He told me that he was doing "Just Fine" in his tent, but I proposed that he buy my cabin for another ten dollars, anyway. He offered seven and while seven dollars is less than a third of what Jake had sold similar cabins for, I was happy that he bought it, for I know that my animals will remain as a team and be housed at the place they have lived for the past half year. Edward had seven silver dollars in his pocket which I gratefully put into my own.

Saturday, March 8, 1862, three days until departure

Today I hiked up to my claim by Kite Lake, not to pan for gold but to retrieve my two jars of gold dust. They were still buried beneath six inches of loose rocks but I had not counted on digging through two feet of snow first. I spent almost a half hour first digging through the ice and snow just to find the right spot. It felt strange to be walking without at least one of my burros, and as I carried the heavy jars back into town, I regretted not digging up my jars when I still owned pack animals.

I took the two nearly full quart jars to Percival Coty at his assayer's office. He took an eyepiece out of his pocket and carefully looked at each scoopful as he emptied the contents. He first measured and then weighed the mostly black sand with its gold colored treasure. He put his eyepiece back into his pocket and looked at me. "Twenty-two dollars and not a penny more."

I may have found a gold buyer at any of the other five assayer's offices in town who could have given me more money, but I do not like to haggle. Twenty-two more dollars in my own pocket along with my other money will bring the total of my assets to nearly five hundred dollars, altogether. I agreed to his offer.

Until a year ago when I started having dreams of great riches, five hundred dollars would have seemed like a fortune. I am happy to be traveling home with this much. This will be enough to purchase twenty-five or so burros and load them with trade goods. I can even afford to have the twenty-five pack saddles made by a saddle maker.

I am no longer a poor farm boy from Missouri. From today on I shall be Thomas Boone, "The Burro Man."

Monday, March 10, 1862, one day until departure

I leave tomorrow. I have spent the last two days wandering around saying goodbye to people and places. Yesterday, I met Will and Scotty at Alma's place for one last cup of coffee and mug of stew. I may not have seen the last of Scotty as he is considering traveling with me as a passenger in Mr. Tabor's wagon. Will plans to stay here until late summer and then go back to his home in Illinois when this war is over.

Today, I visited with Jake at his place in Buckskin Cemetery. This was my hardest farewell to make for I still grieve for him. His final resting place is in a very peaceful spot. There is an abundance of trees to shield his plot from the frequent harsh winds and his grave dominates all others from its place on a little hill. I sat down and talked to Jake as if he was sitting with me on the front stoop of our little cabin. I told him about Lancelot Slade, the fire at the Silver Slipper, and of losing Abel. I told him that the mice in the cabin all had good strong and straight backs. Though she had asked me to keep her last dance performance a secret, I shared with Jake the private exhibition in our cabin of Miss Silverheels' assets. Jake liked that kind of story and could always keep a secret. He surely smiled that toothy smile as I complained about not seeing her as well as I would have liked in that dark and windowless cabin.

Muffin was with me and seemed to know that Jake was with us as she kept nudging his marker with her nose, and Holly lay peacefully at the side of the mound of dirt bordered with smooth stones from the creek.

The whitewashed wooden marker that I had made was holding up well and I read its inscription to Jake out loud,

"Well done, thou good and faithful friend."

As I stood there feeling Jake's presence I looked to the Northeast and beheld the commanding view of Mount Silverheels and I yelled at the top of my voice, "Well done, Miss Silverheels, wherever you are. Well done."

Old Tom

I left on the morning of March 11, 1862 nearly one year from the day I left Grass Creek with Jake to find our fortunes. I had found some of those riches we came west to find and was heading home with the modest fortune of five hundred dollars. This new-found wealth had not come from gold but from the rewards of hard work and a lot of luck. Jake had not been so fortunate, and I missed him dearly.

Horace Tabor's wagon was already hitched up when I arrived at his store, riding Muffin and carrying only my haversack, a canvas bag and a half bag of grain as I had sold most of my gear to miners in need of equipment. I paid the twenty-five dollar fare with the last of my tokens and about five dollars worth of gold dust. In the canvas bag were my clothes and a few odds and ends and the haversack contained my journals and writing supplies.

Scotty Browne was also going home. With his last twenty-five dollars he had paid for his share of the wagon and rode with very little gear other than some clothing and a dozen bottles of whiskey in a wooden crate. He would ride in the back of the wagon to St. Louis and then walk the remaining sixty miles to his home, where he intended to enlist in the Illinois infantry. Scotty had come to Colorado on his horse, but the spotted Indian pony, Brahma, had been stolen and sold by Lancelot Slade. Like that cantankerous burro, Abel, Brahma had simply vanished.

Another traveler was Lawrence Johnson, having booked passage for a trunk load of his belongings while he was to ride alongside on a feisty gray mare named Helen. He had found good fortune panning for gold and had bought an abundance of goods at cut-rate prices from down-on-their-luck miners to take back to his St. Louis home. LJ, as he liked to be called, was perhaps fifty years old and wore a patch over his left eye. Though he had found a rich claim and was finding a goodly amount of gold, he claimed to be "too old to live in these cold, harsh mountains."

We left town at eight o'clock in the morning with absolutely no fanfare. No one, other than the Tabors, was even there to say goodbye.

George Mills drove the wagon being pulled by four large draft horses. He was to drive it to St. Louis in four weeks, buy supplies, rest the horses for a week and then, for safety, secure passage with a freight train back to Colorado. Mr. Tabor wanted him to be gone for no more than nine weeks.

Scotty rode in the back of the wagon with our gear and his bottles of whiskey. As he loaded his crate onto the wagon he held that familiar finger up and started to say "Whiskey..." I interrupted and said "We know!...We know!"

Richard Hamilton rode with us on the first leg to Denver where he had some business to do with the Rocky Mountain News.

LJ and I followed riding on our horses, and Holly followed behind us barking. As we were to travel at a fairly fast pace, Holly would get to ride much of the time in the back of the wagon with Scotty and his whiskey. LJ and I would take turns riding "shotgun" beside George to give our horses a rest and to protect the wagon from Indians or robbers.

We had traveled less than a half mile when we came upon the Spanish arrastra. Salvador had returned with the trickle of spring run-off and was again working his pulverizing process. The burro pulling the heavy grinding stone around and around in that cold wet circle was not his old friend Orito but was that cantankerous Jackass, Abel. My first impulse was to claim my property and demand a fair payment of fifteen or more dollars, but when I saw the affection being dealt to Abel I rose in my saddle and yelled, "God bless you Salvador!"

He took off that wide sombrero he always wore and yelled his reply "Vaya con Dios, mi amigo!"

I traveled on in peace knowing that Abel would be well cared for. I turned around one last time as the pleasant town of Buckskin Joe disappeared from sight. Holly barked her excitement for she could sense my eagerness to be on a new journey. I now had more adventures to experience, family to visit, and, hopefully, Becky to court. Life again was good.

Wednesday, March 12, 1862

We traveled twenty-five miles today and are now camped on the north edge of that large flat grassy plain surrounded by mountains that some call "The South Park." It was the most grueling twenty-five miles I have ever traveled, even though I was riding Muffin and not walking. The wind did not stop blowing all day and though the sky was blue above us, the ever-howling wind kept the snow stinging at our faces as if we were in a blizzard.

As all animals and travelers were exhausted, we stopped for the day well before sundown, fed the animals extra grain, and huddled inside this canvas-covered wagon. I am glad to have Mrs. Hultgren's lamp along, for it adds light inside our crude shelter with which to write. George built a fire inside an iron kettle, and though it is quite smoky in here, it is warm enough to write in this journal if I toast my fingers by the flames every few minutes.

Sitting under this canvas covering with me is Richard writing an essay for his newspaper, George whittling a whistle or something out of a piece of pine, LJ awkwardly strumming on a banjo, and Scotty having a good time with his whiskey.

We are still quite high in the mountains and it is very cold and windy. Richard says that the French called this treeless highlands that we traveled through today "Bayou Salada" because the ground contains many salty marshes. He says that this flat grassy area was once the bottom of a large inland sea, but I do not believe him. I think that in an attempt to sound educated he often says the craziest things. If we have many more winters such as this last one, I should think it possible to fill it up with a few hundred feet of snow in just a few years as long as it doesn't blow away in this wind. Whatever the reason is for this grassy plain does not interest me, but the view of the nearby snow covered peaks is truly marvelous. To the southwest is that great white crest so fondly known as Mount Silverheels. There are no settlers for miles, and you cannot see the damage to the earth that has been done by greedy men searching for gold. I wonder if I could start a mule operation here such as my father's back home, or maybe I could start a burro breeding farm in that lush looking grassland. I would then live under the shadows of that great mountain and be truly content. Perhaps my brother Michael could help me.

I must be weary to be thinking such thoughts. I would be alone again. I hate farming. Wind and cold bother me. How do I know that Indians are not out there somewhere waiting for a chance to relieve me of my scalp? I will stick to my plan and become Thomas Boone, the traveling burro man from Missouri.

Tomorrow we must cross a steep mountain pass and begin a slow and winding course down to Denver. I am going to content myself with turning around once we reach the top of that pass. I will then take my hat off and wish my favorite mountain and the area she protects a heartfelt "Goodbye for now." I am going to sleep now, though sleeping while sitting up in a crowded wagon with four noisy men and the wind howling outside will not be easy.

Saturday, March 15, 1862

We arrived in Denver City at about noon today. George had business to tend to for Mr. Tabor and told us to meet him at the livery tomorrow morning two hours after daybreak. Denver City seems to be a much warmer place than Buckskin Joe, for the temperatures in this warm March sun are much like a pleasant September day in the mountains. No one yet has explained to my satisfaction why it gets colder when you climb up into the mountains and warmer when you descend.

It took me only a few minutes to find Auntie Martha and Mason, and I did this by asking directions to a wash house. Auntie Martha gave me a hug as she would have given a long lost son, and I welcomed an embrace that I could not have received a year ago in Missouri. She took the news of Jake's passing with great sadness. "Lordy...Lordy," she repeated over and over. I was invited to spend the night in her wash house which is no more than a wood shed attached to the rear of a fine two-story hotel. In a cage made of old soap boxes are four chickens that Auntie Martha said she traded for laundering an old mountain man's clothing. I smiled when she told me of that crusty old man spitting as he negotiated the trade. She keeps the place warm by building small fires under that old tin washtub that she has carried with her all the way from her days of slavery in Kentucky. The steam rising from the water keeps the place quite toasty. Smoke exits the shack by means of a tin stove pipe through the shed roof. One of Mason's jobs is to keep the small fire going in a pit dug into the dirt floor. The floors are shiny black, and the walls are papered with old newspapers which have been pasted on with flour and water. While her home and wash house is confined to simply one ten foot by twelve foot room, the place is not only warm but tidy and comfortable. Tonight I will sleep on a feather and grass stuffed mattress instead of the cold, hard earth.

Two days a week Auntie Martha turns that old tub into an oven by covering it with a heavy piece of tin. Mason fills the tub with pieces of meat scraps, usually beef, that he can purchase at any butcher. Many travelers are hungry and nearly broke by the time they arrive here and happily sell their oxen for a good price. Ox meat, as well as buffalo meat from the grasslands, is so abundant here that Mason can buy brisket, ribs, and other less desirable cuts for just a few pennies. Martha slow cooks this meat for two days with onions, salt, and ample quantities of pepper and calls the resulting soft and spicy meat a word that sounds like "barburcooly," but I do not know how to spell it much less pronounce it like she does. Though it is not "pig pickins" as she would prefer, the fiery beef or buffalo mixture is quite popular here, and the hotel accepts a few pounds a month as rent for her shack and firewood. The rest she sells for a reasonable price, and Martha earns more income from the "barburcooly" than she does from washing clothes. Tonight we had a dinner of her spiced meat and beans, and I found the meal to be quite tasty.

"Why you smiling chile?" Auntie Martha asked as I took my second helping.

I did not tell her that I was getting satisfaction knowing that my father and others would be appalled that I was enjoying "slave food" in the company of two black people who I now considered to be among my dearest friends.

Most people in this town do not seem to care that Mason and Martha have dark skin, and the two are respected as they never have been before. There are, however, some here who brought their old attitudes with them about the colored race, so the two still keep their heads low when walking about town.

Until today, I had believed Denver City to be on the edge of the mountains, but it was a two hour ride east of the mouth of the canyon. What a bustling city this is! Like Buckskin Joe there is the sound of saws and hammers everywhere as large wooden buildings are being built to replace flimsy shacks, and shacks are being built to replace tents. Most businesses and many homes have glass for windows and real door hinges made of brass or iron.

I went with Richard to talk to the owners of the <u>Rocky Mountain News.</u> He wore his black suit, black stove pipe hat, and spectacles and appeared to be sophisticated and very well educated. Richard likes to use big words, and I think he wants to somehow merge the two newspapers or sell some of his essays to them. It was at the news office that I heard reports of the conflict back East. News now arrives from the East in just a few days by means of stagecoaches and may soon arrive almost instantaneously once telegraph lines are completed. Battles back there are getting larger and larger, and it seems as if the whole country will soon be engulfed in a great war. Missouri remains with the Union though politicians have declared allegiance to each side. Many Missourians have enlisted in the Union Army, and perhaps even a larger number have become Confederate soldiers. Pro-Union bands of men raid and burn Confederate-leaning towns and farms and Southern sympathizers raid and burn Union towns and farms. As Grass Creek is a town with strong anti-slavery sentiments, I guess that it is not a safe place to be right now, but I still want to go home. I pray that my family and friends are all out of harm's way.

Everyone here in Denver is very concerned about reports of an army from Texas heading north to capture Colorado gold. Posters are nailed to every available tree or fence urging men to volunteer for a Colorado militia. A brass band plays all day long in a small wooded park near Cherry Creek to stoke up the fires in young hearts brave enough to fight this rebel band. Six hundred soldiers marched out of here a week ago and, as more units are formed, they march out of town to catch up with this army. Scotty Browne liked the idea of a dollar signing bonus, a horse to ride, and twelve dollars a month for three months. He immediately enlisted and was presented with a blue-dyed wool jacket with a yellow ribbon on the sleeve to wear, a rifled musket to carry, and a brown gelding to ride.

George gave Scotty twenty of his twenty-five dollars back and said, "There are dozens of men here willing to pay for a ride to Saint Louis. It was a pleasure riding this far with you."

Scotty took a bottle of whiskey out of his crate and gave it to George. "Have ye a delightful time with this," he said as he held up that index finger. "Whiskey will get you through times o' nae money...."

George interrupted... "I know...I know... better than money will get you through times o' nae whiskey.'"

As Soldier Browne walked towards his horse carrying that crate, a very tall and muscular man of about forty years walked up to him and identified himself as Major John Chivington. He was dressed in what appeared to be a hastily tailored blue uniform as the trousers and the coat did not match in color. "You won't be needing this where you are going, soldier," he said, and took the crate. Scotty immediately protested and said he was "hereby and now resigning from the Colorado Militia."

Major Chivington pulled out a pistol and glared at the skinny Scotsman, "Mount your horse immediately, or I will string you up by the neck and have your body used for target practice." Scotty hopped up on that brown gelding with a very distressed look on his face.

Seeing all this happen, George went back to the wagon and came back in a few seconds carrying Mr. Hultgren's old army canteen. "What are you doing with my canteen?" I asked.

"I'll give you the five dollars I made off of Scotty and you can buy a dozen new ones; just help me pour this bottle of whiskey into it." I agreed and George emptied the water onto the ground and held the canteen while I poured the "devil's drink" into it. He put the wood stopper back on and yelled, "Wait a minute Scotty, you forgot your water!" Scotty gave him a puzzled look while George ran up to the forlorn soldier. "What err ye sayin?" asked Scotty, "I got me water right here in this old clay jug."

"That jug can break and what would you do then?" George asked as he held the old tin water container up by its strap. "This canteen will get you through times of war better than war will get you through times of no canteens."

Scotty thanked him and strung it over the horn of his saddle. We stood with a small crowd of onlookers as the column of mounted soldiers formed. In a few minutes Scotty grabbed the canteen, opened it and took a drink. He straightened in his saddle as if a cat had just landed on his back and turned around to see if we were still there. The skinny soldier in his blue dyed jacket smiled when he saw us, and gave us a crisp salute in military style. Imitating the way Scotty always stood when he gave his silly advice, George and I just stood there looking very serious with our index fingers pointing to the sky.

An officer at the head of the column yelled "Company Ho," and the unit of perhaps thirty of these newly-recruited horse soldiers rode south out of town to meet that Confederate army marching up from Texas.

Richard will stay a few days in Denver and then find a ride back to Buckskin Joe. That leaves just me, LJ, and George to travel east unless George can find more passengers. There are many homesick and weary men wishing for a ride home, but few men still have the

twenty–five dollars for the fare. We will leave in the morning and hope to travel at a rate of forty to fifty miles a day. We will take the Platte River Route, and I expect to be in Grass Creek in less than three weeks.

Sunday, March 16, 1862

I am not fifty miles east of Denver as I should be by this hour. Instead I am about fifty miles south with no hope of seeing Missouri soon.

This morning I awoke fresh and eager in Auntie Martha's modest shack. My clothes had been cleaned and somehow dried and pressed while I slept, and Auntie Martha had already prepared a breakfast of bacon, eggs, coffee and fresh baked bread by the time I awoke. The morning was warm and sunny, and I did not even need to wear a coat though it is only the middle of March. Goodbyes were easy for I had told Mason and Martha to expect me back in a couple of months with fresh supplies from Missouri. I promised Mason a new mouth organ from St. Louis and Auntie Martha a bolt of blue calico cloth. I whistled as I walked with Holly to the livery to get Muffin and meet up with George and the wagon for it felt as if this would be a glorious day.

As we were hitching up the team to the wagon, Major Chivington rode up to us on horseback. Following him were four riders carrying muskets and wearing blue-dyed jackets with yellow ribbons sewed to the arms.

"I hereby declare this wagon and these horses to be property of the Colorado militia," he yelled.

George grabbed his rifle and yelled back, "This wagon and these horses are the property of Horace Tabor of Buckskin Joe, and we are leaving for Saint Louis in two minutes." He hopped on the buckboard and grabbed the reins. Within a second, four muskets and Chivington's pistol were pointed at George's head. Chivington nodded to Lawrence and said, "The militia does not need old blind soldiers," and motioned him away with his revolver. To George he said, "The Rebel army has seized Albuquerque and is heading towards Fort Union. Within the hour you shall have this wagon loaded with supplies and commence immediately south to supply our soldiers heading that way. He pointed to me and said, "...and you will be his mounted escort."

"I'm from Missouri," I said. "We're not in this war."

"You're from Colorado, soldier. I see that you have a horse. Do you own a weapon?" I nodded, and he presented us with enlistment papers to "fill out or else." I glanced at the papers and saw that we were assigned to the Quartermaster core until our services were "....no longer necessary for the supply of essential provisions for the army."

"Mr. Tabor will be compensated for his wagon." He handed George a piece of paper and said, "Fill this supply order from that warehouse and catch up with the militia heading south in one week or less. I will know when you arrive for I shall be leading the First Colorado Volunteers as soon as I catch up with them."

He hesitated and then spat on the ground. "If you are late you will be court marshaled. If you try to desert, I will string you up by the neck and use your bodies for target practice."

We had heard that line before, and we both just nodded.

"Do we get that dollar signing bonus?" George asked.

Major Chivington glared at him, spat on the ground, and rode away.

We found the supplies we were to transport, mostly heavy bags of oats for horses, cornmeal to feed the soldiers, and three crates stamped "Fort Laramie." In these dusty boxes were hardtack crackers presumably from the early days when the fort was a supply post for soldiers protecting travelers heading to the California gold rush. George called them "worm castles" or "molar breakers."

Within an hour we were heading south. I rode Muffin beside the wagon and eight newly recruited "volunteers" were riding in the wagon on top of the bags of grain. All we have to guide us is a crudely-drawn map and orders to deliver our goods to the militia heading south within a week. No one said a word about Holly so we smuggled her onto the wagon as she could not keep up with the brisk pace we were now forced to travel. I am now in the Colorado militia wearing one of those blue-dyed wool jackets for God knows how long and heading in a direction I do not choose to travel. I do not know when, or even if, I shall see my home again.

Old Tom

Two months before, I had participated in the killing of a man and had resolved to never to fire a gun at a human being again.

I had been heading home to a state considered neutral in this great war that had begun. Now I found myself, scarcely two weeks after my seventeenth birthday, a soldier riding south to a place I had no desire to visit, to defend the area I was leaving, to fight in a dispute which I felt could have been settled without bloodshed.

CHAPTER 13

The Battle of Glorieta Pass

Tuesday, March 18, 1862

This is day three of a journey taking me away from Missouri and not to it, for we are on the Santa Fe Trail heading south towards the New Mexico Territory and not east towards home. We traveled another fifty miles today. Ahead of us are the "Spanish Peaks," two large mountains that are on our maps and where Major Chivington told us that we must be by sundown, but they look to be another twenty miles ahead. Our horses will die if we force them on for another mile for they are quite weary and in need of a good rest. I will not write much tonight as I am exhausted as well.

About once every hour today a cavalry officer wearing a blue jacket with yellow stripes would ride by and tell us that our wagon was moving too slowly. George kept the horses moving all day long at a good clip but refused to "drive them to death." At sundown, we encountered a train of five wagons also heading with supplies to Fort Union. We camp with them tonight, and from now on we will travel with them for safety.

Wednesday March 19, 1862

At about noon today our group of wagons came upon a militia group of about twenty blue-shirted soldiers briskly marching south. That same cavalry officer was there and demanded that we carry these men so that they may soon catch up with the rest of the army that left Denver two weeks ago. George and the other drivers protested that our wagons were already overloaded but that all too familiar six-shooter was drawn and pointed. We now have thirteen soldiers riding on top of bags of grain, and the wheels on the wagon creak with the added load.

For dinner tonight, all we had to eat was a handful of hardtack crackers and water. "I just bit something soft in this worm castle!" George yelled.

I immediately put down my cracker. "Is it a maggot?" I asked, fearful that my own hardtack was infested with worms.

"No, I think it's a nail," he joked, and everyone laughed that I had fallen for that old prank.

It is now snowing, and I must move my bedding to under a wagon where I shall be forced to sleep tonight with four or five others all needing a dry place out of the snow and wind.

Thursday, March 20, 1862

It is still snowing, but tonight I can sleep in a tent provided by the militia. I must share this tent with three other soldiers, and we are quite cramped but dry. It is cold in this tent, but it is much colder outside.

Today we caught up with perhaps a hundred more soldiers marching south towards Fort Union where it is rumored that we will have to face that Confederate army from Texas. I feel blessed for I am riding a horse. George, Scotty, and anyone else fortunate enough to have a horse or wagon to ride on are lucky, as well, when compared to those men who are being forced to march at a rate of twenty-five miles a day in this awful weather. When I walked to Colorado, a good day was one in which we traveled fifteen miles and we did not travel at all when the weather was miserable.

There must be thirty or forty wagons heading from Denver to supply the garrison at Fort Union. Mounted soldiers keep telling us to either hurry up or to wait as they try to get all of those wagons into a compact train. For safety, though I do not see why, we are to ride abreast in rows of four. This means that at any one time three of the wagons might not be on the trail. My job is to escort this "armada of prairie schooners," as we are called, by riding with other mounted soldiers about fifty yards to the right to guard the supplies from an attack from the west. Other escorts ride an equal distance to the left. The hundred, or so, soldiers march at a brisk pace in front of us, also in rows of four. Muffin and I are never on the trail. The cavalry, which includes Scotty, spends all day riding miles around the perimeter of this army to act as the "eyes and ears" of this company known as "The Colorado First." Major Chivington and the four cavalrymen wearing those yellow ribbons occasionally ride up to us, and he will yell some orders and then ride on.

It is two hours after sundown and we have just been told that in one hour we must be ready for a night march over Raton Pass. Soldiers are whispering that the "enemy" must be closer than thought. I will quit writing now and help George get the team ready.

204

Wednesday March 26, 1862

War has now arrived to this part of America. Perhaps somewhere near here men are fighting and dying, and I have nothing to do but stay here with the wagons and worry. We take turns on guard duty, and it is my hour to rest though I keep my scattergun on my lap in case something happens. Perhaps I can relieve the tension by adding to my journal, so I will write about what has happened in the week since I last wrote.

We are now in New Mexico Territory at a ranch near a break in the mountains known as Glorieta Pass. We crossed the very rugged Raton Pass at night and in a blizzard, arrived at Fort Union late the next day, spent one cold night shivering in a tent, and then traveled another seventy-five or so miles to get to this ranch before the army from Texas arrived.

Raton Pass is very rugged, and the forced night march was as grueling an adventure as any that I have ever experienced. Cold snow was blowing the entire night, and the horses struggled to pull the heavy loads. I walked beside Muffin to prevent her from dropping from total fatigue. At least a half dozen horses died from exhaustion, but the army kept moving forward. To keep men from collapsing from the effort, they were ordered to take turns riding on already overloaded wagons. Four or five wagons broke down from the strain, and some nonessential goods were left behind, but we just kept marching on in that cold blowing snow.

Our caravan of wagons and soldiers was the last from the Denver area to arrive at Fort Union. Most Colorado soldiers and supplies arrived a week ago, and many have trickled in daily ever since. The regular army was pleased to see us turn up but not pleased enough to give us quarters in their warm lodges, so the entire Colorado First, including those of us assigned to the quartermaster corps, were forced to sleep out in the cold in those small tents. All of us from up north thought that we would just stay at Fort Union and help defend it from behind walls when the Texans attacked, but it seems that those in charge are eager for battle. We only spent one night at the fort before moving on, getting here to this ranch, seventy-five miles from the fort, in just two days.

The regular army stayed behind at Fort Union and it is up to us, the untrained "volunteers' from Colorado, to do battle with the Texans, and why I do not know. I only know that our commander, a Colonel named Canby, somehow outranks Fort Union's commander. I also know that the regular army officers despise us and think of us as nothing but "mountain ruffians." The night we stayed at the fort, the army storehouse was broken into and quite a few bottles of the officers' whiskey were looted. When we heard this news, George and I laughed, wondering if somehow Scotty was involved.

Last night I also heard that a brigade of a hundred or so Colorado miners had entered camp, coming here not through the plains to the east of the mountains as we had done, but by marching for two hundred and fifty miles straight south through those perilous and snow-filled peaks along an old Indian trail first scouted by Kit Carson. They had performed this miracle march in just two weeks without losing a single man.

Before dawn this morning, all soldiers, cavalrymen, and those of us with the supply train were awakened by a bugle playing a lively tune. The soldiers were soon arranged by company, and I could see that our army was possibly more than a thousand strong.

An old man, probably Colonel Canby though I do not know, sat astride a fine Tennessee riding horse and gave a short and loud speech to fire up the bravery among the hundreds of us standing at attention. About half of the soldiers stood with those childish puffed out chests and about half stood as I did, shaking in our boots out of fear. When the gray haired man yelled, "Today we shall meet the elephant!" the army cheered at yet another use of the elephant saying. I did not cheer once but surely those rebels, if they are as close as reported, heard the commotion.

206

Major Chivington was straddling another Tennessee riding horse and had been ordered to form a battalion and leave immediately with three units of a hundred soldiers each to take a long route around the pass and attack the rebels from the rear. The remaining force of seven to eight hundred soldiers would follow soon after to make a frontal attack on the main force of the Confederate army where it is reported to be encamped just a few miles ahead of us on the other side of Glorieta Pass.

A bugler riding on a chestnut horse next to the major trumpeted a short tune, and I could see the three units approaching. One of the columns was marching to the beat of a drum and to a cadence that was very familiar to me. I could see from a hundred yards away about a hundred or so men dressed, not in the familiar blue-dyed jackets, but simply in mining clothes and leather hats. These men, I thought, were surely that company of miners that everyone was talking about. Leading this brigade was a man dressed in the only regular army uniform that I had seen in these two weeks of army life. What a surprise it was when I recognized that it was none other than Postmaster Henry Dodge of Buckskin Joe, proudly carrying that American flag of his from the Mexican war days. Minnie McKeever, the drunk Irishman, was beating Mr. Dodge's drum to the same rhythm as the daily flag raisings. Those hundred miners, many of them friends of mine, were carrying shotguns, flintlocks, pistols, or whatever weapon they owned and were marching in unison, more or less, to his drumming. Someone had made a battle flag out of a piece of rawhide and some red ribbon. In black charcoal lettering was scrawled the words, "Buckskin Brigade." This battle flag was being carried by "Big Jake" the hardy Minnesotan who had made my snowshoes.

George stood on the top of his buckboard and yelled "Give 'em Hell Buckskin Joe." While Big Jake smiled that silly smile under his rust-red mustache the entire thousand man army roared their approval until Chivington's hands were raised to silence the noise. With Major Chivington and the bugler being the only men astride horses, the force of three hundred armed soldiers including a hundred of my fellow townsmen quietly left camp to sneak around the far side of the enemy.

Under the command of Colonel Edward Canby the remaining force of armed Colorado Territory men left soon after, now as quietly as possible, to face the Texan army headlong.

The regular army wagons carrying equipment necessary for battle, such as ammunition and medical goods followed the Colorado Army, but those of us "hired" to carry non-essential supplies were to remain here hidden behind what few trees were to be found near this adobe-walled ranch. I, along with about twenty other mounted escorts and forty foot soldiers, stayed with these wagon masters to protect the supplies in the fifty-seven wagons. Should the Confederate force break through, we will be no match for their rumored strength.

At about noon we could hear far off gunfire. This noise has continued all day with no word coming to us of the battle's outcome. The sound of thunder that comes every few minutes must be coming from those seven cannons that I saw being pulled by mules.

It is now sundown, and the sound of gunfire and cannons has stopped. I do not know which side won, but the silence is as frightening as the noise was. It may be possible that the Texans have indeed broken through and are now heading our way. We have been ordered to remain quiet with our weapons loaded and ready. No fires are to be built tonight, and we are not uttering a word.

As it starts to get dark, I am leaning against a wagon wheel with my scatter gun on my lap trying to rest, but I will not sleep tonight. No one will.

Friday, March 28, 1862

I did not hear a single gunshot all day yesterday and George, I, and all the drivers and escorts had little to do but wait with our weapons loaded and ready to fight. Though I do not like to admit this, I was afraid all day. I would not have walked away as I did that day when confronting Lancelot Slade, but I did not wish for a fight.

This morning it was the sound of distant cannon fire that woke me up and that noise continued all day long.

Soldiers are now filtering back to the camp. Some are wounded and bandaged up, most are filthy, and all are tired. If these men saw their "elephant" it was certainly not a gentle circus animal pulling a parade wagon but that enormous and terrifying beast with ferocious red eyes. They relate dreadful accounts of a battle that raged this day as men fired weapons at each other at close range for almost seven hours. There are reports of bayonet attacks and fierce hand to hand combat. I hear that a great number of our men were killed and reports are coming that a greater number of the enemy lay dead, as well. A large number from both sides are at this time lying on the battlefield wounded and perhaps freezing to death in this cold March wind. I am saddened that we use the word "enemy" as those Texans, until recently, were our fellow countrymen. I am sadder that anyone, no matter how he views slavery, is out in this cold wind, alone and suffering.

Saturday March 29, 1862

It seems as if neither we nor the Confederates were able to produce a victory, and Federal troops have fallen back to the safety of this adobe-walled ranch. Two hours from now our supply wagons must depart for another ranch in the mountains six miles away and hopefully six miles safer. No one knows where the rebels are, and the fear is that they might attack at any moment. Information is coming back that Chivington with the help of the Buckskin Brigade found a Confederate supply train much like this one and destroyed it. Much as I feared could happen to us, the few Texans guarding those wagons were completely overwhelmed by the First Colorado Infantry. Major Chivington not only ordered all of the wagons and supplies burned, he also ordered the killing of all Confederate horses and mules. What a waste of good animals! Why did he not bring them back for use here or scatter them for the locals to find?

I do not care for this Chivington fellow. Some say he ordered the execution of all rebel prisoners, as well, but that order was not obeyed. Hurray for the Coloradoans who refused that order, if it is true! I hear that Chivington came here from Ohio as a Methodist minister intent on stopping the flow of alcohol. Once when he destroyed some kegs of whiskey he declared, "God and these two six shooters give me this right." When this war broke out, he was offered a place in the militia as a chaplain but refused it and demanded a fighting position. From what I hear about this "Fighting Parson," as he is called, I believe he would have no problem with stringing a deserter up by the neck and using his body for target practice.

With the loss of their supply train it is thought that the Texans should soon run out of supplies and ammunition and may have to fall back or boldly attack us to get our stores. I hope that they fall all the way back to Texas!

Sunday, March 30, 1862

It is morning and I am here at another adobe-walled ranch and am on an uneasy two hour break from guard duty. I did not sleep last night. All of the supply wagons are within these four foot high walls made of mud and straw and all of the horses are penned in a make-shift corral between a barn and one of the adobe walls. Fifty soldiers stand on guard duty for two hours at any given time while another fifty rest. I have been ordered to get some sleep but cannot do so, so I am again writing. We are supposed to be safe at this ranch, but who can rest when he knows that a thousand armed and hungry Texans are out there somewhere?

About two hours ago, near sunrise, one of the sentries saw someone walking in the trees about one hundred yards away. He yelled to the person to identify himself but got no response. I was on guard duty at the time and felt a shiver on my back but was brave enough to run towards the action and not away from it. A corporal in charge of our group of sentries yelled "Fire!" and we all fired our weapons at the lone figure though the only thing my scatter gun could kill would be some hapless squirrel at half that distance. Whoever was out there quickly ran away, and no one chased him, if it was a "him." Whoever was out there will not be coming back alone. If it was a Confederate spy, we have been found and their entire army might soon attack. If it was a deer or a Mexican sheepherder looking for his animals, we just wasted a lot of ammunition and made a lot of noise.

I now know that if that incident had indeed been an attack by the Confederates I would have stood behind that adobe wall and defended my position as ordered instead of turning away in fear as I have in the past. I was expecting hundreds of soldiers to attack from over that hill and I had my scattergun reloaded in seconds. I will not deny that I was plenty excited and perhaps even a little afraid, but I have grown up a little since that day I turned and walked away from Lancelot Slade. If an attack happens I will wait to fire my shot until the rebels are within a few yards. Perhaps that yellow stripe has faded from my back but I still do not wish to pull a trigger to end another man's life. Father will be proud when I tell him I stood my ground but I will not share my reluctance to kill my fellow man.

It has just taken me over an hour to write these few words, and I have guard duty again in less than an hour. First I am to report to the grub wagon for breakfast, but I do not think that I can stomach any more hardtack and weak parched corn coffee. It is assumed that our militia is out chasing the rebels, but no one has heard a report in hours. Rumors are circulating that those Texans are over that hill to the west and are about to attack us to get our supplies. Perhaps, as others are doing, it is time to pin my name on my shirt and write my final letter.

Adobe walled ranch
New Mexico Territory
March 30, 1862

Dear friend,

If you are reading this letter, I likely am seriously wounded or no longer living in this world. I wish to convey on this paper my final wishes.

I determined some time ago that I never again would turn away from danger and I wish it to be known that I stood my ground as commanded and did not back up a single step. If this letter is being read by a Texan, please know that I meant no malice, and perhaps just as you have done, I only followed the orders that were given to me. I sincerely pray that you, the reader of this letter, are an honorable man. Inside the leather cover of my Bible you will find bank notes worth nearly five hundred dollars. Keep what you must for yourself, but please find it in your heart to have my remains shipped to the Buckskin Cemetery to be buried alongside my friend Jake Lewis.

I have addressed an envelope for the mailing of a letter to my family in Grass Creek, Missouri . Please tell them of my fate and how my last thoughts and prayers were for them and for my special friend Becky Thompson.

My final request is to please cherish as I did a chestnut horse named Muffin and a brown dog named Holly.

May you, the reader of this letter, have a long and fruitful life.

Thomas Boone, age 17 years
Buckskin Joe, Colorado Territory

Tuesday, April 1, 1862

The fighting may be over! The Texas army is perhaps not going to attack after all and is reported to have retreated all the way back to Santa Fe! Travelers and merchants are still using the Santa Fe Trail as if nothing noteworthy or dangerous is happening. They tell us that the rebels did not lose an inch of ground during the battle and perhaps even pushed back the Colorado assault, but the Confederates have little in the way of supplies and ammunition to continue their invasion. These brave and foolish trekkers know this because the Texans are begging or stealing food from teamsters as they continue on the trail.

Great cheering and celebrating is going on here, and officers are giving us hourly speeches congratulating each other, and themselves, for their bravery. It was actually blind luck and the bravery of those miners from Buckskin Joe that turned the tide of the battle. Instead of out-flanking the Texans as ordered, they fortunately happened upon a supply train such as ours and completely overran its defenders before destroying it. During a ten minute skirmish the southern defenders fired only a few volleys before realizing their hopeless situation and easily gave up. Only one of the hardy miners was killed in the assault, and I am distressed to learn that it was the flag-bearer, Big Jake. I am deeply saddened by this loss. He was such a gentle giant of a man. He walked into that battle not carrying a weapon but proudly holding only that crudely made buckskin flag. I like to think that he passed from this world with that silly smile on his face, but I doubt anyone can smile when bullets are flying. I hope that his sacrifice will make this horrifying conflict come to an end a bit sooner, and today is soon enough for me to end all this hostility.

I often wonder how many more friends I shall lose in this dreadful war that is now taking place over much of this land. I wonder if I will die.

Sunday, April 13, 1862 and a very good day!

This is the last page in the journal and I am out of paper to continue writing but this seems to be a fine day to stop writing and concentrate on heading east.

We are heading home! Scotty and all soldiers who enlisted in the militia must stay here to guard the Territory until the end of the war, but those like George and me who were forcefully mustered into the quartermaster corps to supply the soldiers are free to leave. I did not wish to be a soldier and it seems as if I participated in this Civil War, as they now call it, with only the quite annoying inconvenience of having to go a few hundred miles out of my way and eating bad food. We happily gave back our blue-dyed shirts and hope to never wear such clothing again.

I have a desperate desire to go home, and George needs to travel to Saint Louis for merchandise for Mr. Tabor. We are already three weeks behind schedule, so we chose to leave at once even though it was the middle of the afternoon. We each received a piece of paper redeemable in Denver for ten dollars for our troubles and George received a note for ten dollars to give Mr. Tabor for the use of his horses and wagon. George put his notes in his shirt pocket and I put mine in my journal. When we were only about two miles east of this afternoon's departure, George pulled his paper out of his shirt, crumpled it up, and tossed it on the ground where it immediately blew away in the cold April wind. "Worthless piece of trash," he mumbled, and then whipped his horses to travel a bit faster. Muffin sensed his excitement and eagerly picked up her pace as well.

I am now at the bottom of the page and I will finish with these few words: I am no longer a soldier. Life is good again. I am going home!

Old Tom *(fifty years later)*

September 1, 1912

I am sitting on my daughter Christina's porch as I now live with her in her brick bungalow north of town. I have moved many times in the past half century, but I shall not move again. The view from my old chair is westward towards my beloved mountains. In the near distance below those snow capped peaks is the Cache La Poudre River and a half dozen orchards scattered among irrigated fields of grain. This porch with its splendid panorama is an ideal place to sit back and reflect on a wonderful life.

I made it back to Missouri and returned to Colorado just two months later with twenty-six burros, and a mule-drawn wagonload of trade goods. I took those goods and burros straight into the mining country where, in just a few weeks, I sold everything but the wagon and mules to miners in need of my inventory. I repeated that trip once or twice a year for the next six years until the railroads came.

It is estimated that the mountains of Colorado are today inhabited by almost ten thousand burros. In nine trips over the Great Plains, I brought almost two hundred of those delightful animals here and perhaps a very large percentage of that ten thousand are descended from my stock. After the coming of the railroads, the transporting of goods and animals by overland routes became unprofitable and I moved permanently to Colorado, eventually settling in this fine little college town of Fort Collins in 1877, the year after Colorado became a state and the year I started a hotel by the railroad tracks. I named that hotel Jake's Place. My thirty-year-old son, Jacob Lewis Boone, runs that hotel and restaurant today, and it is doing quite well.

I have finished assembling my diary, and until recently, I thought that the story of my early days in Colorado was complete. I quit writing in my journals shortly after that skirmish with the Texans that some today call "The Gettysburg of the West," and I did not pick up a pen again for years. Nearly everyone who has read my manuscript

215

tells me "This book is not finished until you write about Becky." I can see, that though I quit writing in a diary, this book is missing a very important chapter of my early adventures. That missing chapter is of Becky and my return to Missouri in early 1862.

Becky

After the battle of Glorieta Pass, George and I followed the Santa Fe Trail eastward for nearly three weeks, averaging almost fifty miles a day in our hurry to get home. Because of the fast pace we traveled, Holly and I rode in the wagon while Muffin followed behind. George had grown so fond of Holly that he did not want her to run so much, so when it was time to leave the trail, George went forty miles out of his way to take us all the way into Grass Creek. We arrived three hours before sundown on May 2, 1862, thirteen months and one day after I had walked proudly westward with Jake in the lead. The town remained largely unchanged, but I had returned a completely different person. I was older, wiser, and in my opinion, a better person than the mere boy who had so naively left the area searching for adventure.

Though I offered to put George up for the night, he refused and continued on towards St. Louis. A handshake and "We'll meet again," was all that either of us offered each other after experiencing eight weeks of travel and war together. Holly whined as he drove away, but I was eager to get home and I had much to do before going those last two miles.

The first thing I noticed about Grass Creek was that Mr. Groom's store was missing and a new one was being built in its place, though no one was working on it on that day. The charred remains of the old store lay in a pile behind the new one. I pondered the new store for a minute, sure that Mr. Groom had been punished for openly support-ing Abraham Lincoln, and then I went to the Lewis Hotel, leaving Holly and Muffin resting outside. Jake's parents had received my let-ter, and his mother cried when she saw me. She gave me a motherly embrace but said, "You need to go home at once," and refused to say why. She only said, "It's not good." I gave her the two hundred dollars that Jake had saved. She nodded her appreciation, gave me another hug and said, "Please, you must go home."

"Jake willed Muffin to me before he died," I added.

She again nodded, "Go home."

As I hurried out of town, I could see eight graves being dug by about twice that many men in the small cemetery behind the church. Though Muffin was tired after a fifty-mile ride, I hastened her on our remaining two miles, hoping desperately that none of those graves was for anyone who was dear to me. Mrs. Lewis was clearly holding back terrible news but would not share it. I would not stop first at the Thompson farm as I had planned. I could wait one more day to see Becky, but perhaps, because I was soon to pass by her house, I might catch a glimpse of her.

As I neared the Thompson farm, I saw only smoke and little else. The corn crib of our adventure was gone, the barn was gone, and like the corn crib and barn, the house had also burned to a smoking

218

pile of charred timbers and ashes. I yelled, "Becky" but there was no answer. The only presence in the air was that awful smoke that filled my body with terror.

I hurried Muffin now to a gallop and raced the remaining half mile home. Holly couldn't keep up with our fast pace, but she now knew the way and followed as fast as she could.

Mother had seen me coming as I approached and ran quickly out of the house. I hopped off of Muffin and ran to her. She was crying but gave me a warm embrace. "Bushwackers burned the Thompson farm last night!"

She paused. "Your father and the five other men who went there to help Mr. Thompson defend his property were killed in the raid."

She paused again. "They also killed Becky's parents, and ran off with the livestock."

I had just been told that my father was dead. I should possibly have acted more disturbed, but the first words out of my mouth were "Where's Becky?" Mother motioned towards the door, and I raced inside.

Becky was sitting at the table with her head on it when I entered. She looked up when she heard the door open, sprang to her feet, and wrapped her arms around my neck. It was the greeting I had dreamed of but not exactly under the circumstances I had wanted.

She spoke when the words could come between sobs: "Both of my brothers left home last week to join the Union army ... Rebels came to punish my family... Robert Masters heard rumors of the raid and rode here to warn us... Mother made me run to your house for safety, but she stayed behind with my father... Your father... Mr. Masters... Mr. Groom... and three other men with muskets were no match for twenty well-armed and trained raiders... Dead, all of them, dead... They even murdered Mother."

I just held her as she cried. I cried, too.

Becky remained at our house while Michael, Holly, and I slept in the barn. She and my mother soon busied themselves with preparations for a mass funeral in just two days. They wrote things they wanted Reverend Johnson to say; they cooked together; they baked together; they cried together. Mostly I helped Michael around the farm, but I tried to be there for Mother and Becky as often as I could.

The funeral was held on a Saturday. People for miles around came to pay their respects for the seven men and one woman who had been so senselessly murdered. As the congregation that day was quite large, the funeral was held outside in the cool early May wind. I stood up front with the families of the deceased between Mother and Becky while holding each of their hands tightly in my own. Michael held my mother's other hand. I remember nothing of the words Reverend Johnson was delivering. I only remember staring at the eight wooden coffins and thinking about the brutality of this war. I missed my father and regretted that I would never have a chance to apologize for my eagerness to leave the farm. He had not ridden to his death to find glory; he had only gone to the defense of a friend. Becky's parents had done nothing wrong other than to raise two sons who had gone off to fight for a cause they believed in. Becky's mother was perhaps the sweetest woman I had ever met. She had died with that ever present calico apron on and had committed no offense greater than staying at home with her husband.

The eight caskets were lowered by ropes into eight holes, one after the other, in the little cemetery behind the church. Reverend Johnson said a prayer each time. I cried during Reverend Johnson's prayer for my father as his casket descended into that cold, dark hole. Becky and my mother cried all eight times.

We lingered around the church for a few hours and did not arrive home until nearly dark. Becky came with us as if she were a part of the family. We all sat around and talked about good memories of our

*departed loved ones until well after midnight when Michael and I
retired to our beds on the hay.*

*A week later I gave my mother a hug and said, "I've decided to
stay home and run this farm."*

*"For a solid week you have been telling me stories of mountains,
sunshine, blue skies and huge stars," she replied, "and have been
talking nearly nonstop about those silly donkeys you now call burros.
You have bigger fish to fry than staying on this farm."*

"What does that mean?"

*"I knew before your tenth birthday that you could never be a
farmer. Michael is a farmer, and you are an adventurer. This farm
would only hold you down. Becky is an adventurer as well. When the
two of you were children, we could not keep either of you out of trees
or caves. Surely you must see what I see."*

I did, or at least I thought that I understood what she said.

"She needs you."

I knew that, as well, or at least I had hoped that she might.

*Becky and I were married just four weeks later on a Sunday, fol-
lowing the morning church service. She was only sixteen years old,
and I was seventeen. Until that very special day, I continued to sleep
in the barn.*

*During those same four weeks I made preparations for my return
to Colorado by collecting as many burros and trade goods as I could
afford. I put out the word that I would buy donkeys for two dollars a
head, pack saddles for two dollars each, and donkey carts for four
dollars, prices all far greater than their current values. I used much
of my five hundred dollars to buy supplies and merchandise which
I could sell for huge profits in the gold country. I traveled to Saint
Louis to buy four crates of glass cut into six inch squares to make*

windows to replace the oiled canvas windows popular in the mountains. I bought two crates of books, magazines, and dime novels to help bored and lonely men find a way to pass the time. I even bought a crate of musical instruments including Ozark jaw harps, mouth organs and four or five fiddles, for music is as much desired as spirits to ease the pains of loneliness. Women around Grass Creek knitted warm wool socks, mittens, and caps which I eagerly purchased as well as dried fruits and nuts.

Becky stayed in the house while she and Mother made plans for the wedding, and consoled each other as they mourned their losses. All Becky's possessions had been destroyed in the fire, including that pretty blue dress. Though the war had caused shortages of cotton cloth, Mother found half a bolt of blue fabric the color of a Colorado sky as well as some white lace and sewed a new outfit for her to wear. As it was to serve as her wedding dress, I was forced to wait until our big day to see it. Becky made her own white wedding veil, and I could not see that either.

After what seemed like an eternity, the day of our wedding, June 6, 1862, finally came. I was not allowed to see her that morning and rode Muffin to my own wedding while Mother, Michael, and Becky all rode in the buggy. Michael stood with me outside the church to listen through a half open window, as Reverend Johnson delivered his sermon so that I would not see my bride.

"Ridiculous tradition," I remember thinking, but when I was summoned into the church after the sermon, I saw Becky standing up front wearing that new blue dress with a white wedding veil and forgot all about my impatient wait. She was more beautiful than any woman I had ever seen before, Miss Silverheels included.

Reverend Johnson performed a simple wedding with about fifty people in attendance. I do not remember a word of what he said that morning. I just kept staring at Becky with joy in my heart over how lucky I was to now have her in my life forever. I think that Mother was joyous, as well, but she sat crying in the front row for the entire ceremony. A reception was held immediately following the service at the Lewis Hotel. Jake's mother gave us the gift of "the best room in the house" for an entire week along with free dinners as a very generous wedding present.

Mother came up to Becky and me as the guests were leaving and said, "I'm giving you the wagon and those two young mules you wanted. I protested that she and Michael would need them for the farm.

Mother put her finger to her lips and said, "You need them far more than we do."

Traditionally the eldest son inherits the family farm upon a father's death, but I said, "Michael deserves to keep the farm." She nodded her approval.

One week later I was ready to once again leave Missouri and head to the Colorado Territory. I had assembled my own outfit consisting of that fine wagon covered with a sturdy canvas, two burros pulling carts, and twenty-four burros with loaded pack saddles on their backs. I had found six young and eager Colorado-bound fortune seekers who had horses, but not much else, who were quite willing to ride alongside the caravan and help. I would provide them with food, security, and knowledge of the route; they would provide me with help and protection.

It was on Monday, June 14, 1862, that I got my strange caravan loaded and ready for a second voyage out of Grass Creek with the morning sun at my back. The pack burros were arranged into four trains of six and were each led by a mounted rider. Each burro carried two bags containing either grain or an assortment of merchandise including warm socks, wool hats, gloves and an abundance of peppermint candy. The other two riders were leading the donkey carts. One cart had been modified to serve as a small cook wagon and the other carried kegs of water. I proudly sat on the wagon leading the procession. Two of the finest gray mules in the country were eagerly waiting to start pulling that heavy cargo. Muffin was following behind, led by a rope tied to the back of the wagon. On this trip Muffin would only have to carry her saddle and nothing else, for she had earned that privilege.

As she would be so often for the next forty-eight years, my beloved Becky was at my side.

She was eager to see all those places I had told her about, and she was quite willing to leave the charred memories of her family farm miles behind her.

Holly could sense that another adventure was about to begin and was barking at the heels of the burros as if to get them moving on their way. Because of the faster pace we would travel this time, I had made a wooden extension to the back of the wagon for her to ride on when she wearied from walking. She proudly rode on this simple pine platform as if she were Cleopatra being carried on a golden litter. From her perch she could watch all that was happening and bark at the burros or passersby whenever she felt the need to do so.

Mother and Michael came to the hotel early that morning to see us off. As I sat on that buckboard, I assured Mother that we would be home again before the snow returned, and she smiled her agreement. She did not cry this time. Though we had already made our farewells on the ground, Michael helped her up onto the buckboard for one last hug, and she again gave Becky an embrace with equal motherly love. "Now, go fry those fish," she said as Michael helped her off the heavily loaded wagon.

We had traveled only about a hundred yards when Reverend Johnson saw us approaching the church. He yelled for us to stop so that he might bless us on our journey, and we obeyed.

"Where are you heading with this strange outfit?"

"To find our future!" I proudly exclaimed.

"Have you charted a path to that future?" he asked, perhaps wanting to steer me to a religious conversation.

"We plan to travel due west out of town for six hundred miles. Once we pass an old mountain man's trading post, we will travel through two hundred miles of short prairie grass with absolutely no water. At the mountains we will follow a river until it becomes so narrow that the trees reach out to hug each other and from there we will follow a pleasant little stream until it meets the sky."

He looked puzzled. "I'm not familiar with your route. Does it have a name?"

"Name? Why of course it does! I call it.....

"The Road to Buckskin Joe"

My Road to Buckskin Joe

Author and "Me Too" in Fairplay (1978)

Much of this story is based on actual people and places. There really was a boom town called Buckskin Joe in the 1860's near the present town of Alma, Colorado. Horace and Augusta Tabor (two important characters of Colorado history) arrived with two wagon loads of goods in 1861. Father Dyer arrived there soon after to preach "fire and brimstone" to the miners, and landmarks in nearby Breck-enridge, Fairplay, and Leadville still carry his name to this day. In March, 1862 Major John Chivington, under the command of Col. John P. Slough, led a militia of Colorado miners to the New Mexico territory to fight a Confederate army from Texas. He later gained infamy when he led an attack on a sleeping and undefended Indian

226

village, near Sand Creek, Colorado. There his militia massacred more than one hundred Cheyenne and Arapahoe women and children, and took their scalps to Denver to be displayed. Auntie Martha was based on the real Auntie Clara Brown who, upon her freedom, hired on as a cook on a wagon train in 1859 and settled in Central City where she ran a wash house and earned enough money to help transport to Colorado and find work for up to twenty-six other former slaves. Most other characters in this book are named for friends and bear little resemblance to a historical person.

A dance hall girl, known to the ages as "Silverheels" also, as legend tells, arrived in 1861, nursed miners back to health during a small pox epidemic, and lives on to this day in local lore. Dance hall girls were not necessarily as promiscuous as they are portrayed in movies and made a living by talking to the miners and dancing with them for a small fee. Often these girls were widows stranded in the West or wives and sisters of the dance hall operators. Though they possibly made considerably less than some so-called "ladies of the evening," they made good money, held standing in their communities, attended church, and often looked down upon the common prostitute. Any person living today near what once was the town of Buckskin Joe will correct you if you compare Miss Silverheels to a movie temptress who lures customers up a set of stairs to her bed. When I lived in the area in the 1970's and early 1980's, there were numerous places and businesses honoring her name. Mount Silverheels to the Northeast is the most prominent, but there was also Silverheels Bar, Silverheels Ranch, Silverheels Subdivision, and so on. An annual Miss Silverheels contest was, until recently, held each year in Fairplay, with the winner being honored with a ride on a float in the annual "Burro Days" parade. I built mountain cabins back then under the name Silverheels Construction. I found no written records of Silverheels in my research, just legends written years after her departure. I hope I have kept her mystery and honor intact, for though I have been gone from the area for over twenty-five years, I am still smitten with her.

Burros were an important part of the mining community and were used in and around Colorado mines until World War II. Some burros were set free when the miners left, and they roamed the streets of Fairplay and Alma, begging at doors for food until the 1950's. In Cripple Creek these animals continued to freely roam until the 1990's. Outside the high school in Fairplay is a bronze sculpture of its mascot, a fully loaded pack burro, and sports teams there are known as the "South Park Burros." Fairplay, Buena Vista, Leadville, and sometimes Breckenridge and Cripple Creek, all host burro races honoring their mining heritage.

I attempted the "World Championship" race in Fairplay in 1978. My burro, "Me Too," was loaded with the required thirty-three pounds of mining gear, and I was connected to her by a fifteen foot long rope which I used gently as a whip as I ran along beside. The tee shirt I was wearing said: "If you can't get your ass up the pass, come to the J Bar J," a local watering hole owned by a real "Big Al." My ass made it over the pass and we completed twenty-four of the thirty treacherous miles when Me Too tuckered out, kneeled down, and refused to budge another inch. By then, we were in last place anyway, and the official race veterinarian pulled us from the competition. Friends awaiting my return at the J Bar J came and got my ass.

A six mile foot race in the winter of 1979, very similar to the one near the end of the book including generous quantities of alcohol, took place between a real Bill Reeves and me. I lost that one as well. Richard Hamilton, the owner/editor of *The Fairplay Flume* was very much a part of the event and helped to turn a drunken rivalry into a charity event which has run yearly since then, generating thousands of dollars for local causes. The now official 10K race is held the third Saturday in August under the name "Ed Snell Memorial Run/Walk," named for a local businessman, who as a young man, ran a burro train such as the one in this book. Twenty percent of the gross sales of this book go to help fund this, my favorite, charity.

A story that developed during my research that I couldn't find a place to tell in this book is that of the Tabors. Horace and Augusta Tabor had already acquired and saved a fair sum of money by the time they arrived in 1861 by following gold strikes and the resulting influx of treasure seekers. Horace was a likeable fellow but not a good businessman. Augusta was hard working, shrewd, and frugal and was reputed to be the brains behind their success. Together they would cook meals and otherwise supply miners for a 30% share of their claims. While most men found very little in the way of riches, a few found very profitable claims and the Tabors were, within a few years, among the wealthiest couples in the nation.

A flamboyant man, Horace deserted Augusta for Elizabeth McCourt, 25 years his junior, in 1880. Augusta left for California with perhaps a few hundred thousand dollars, while Horace kept most of the multi-million dollar fortune. The public and the press became enamored with the new couple and referred to Elizabeth as "Baby Doe." Their extravagant lifestyle became front page news across the nation, and they lived lavishly until the silver panic of 1893 wiped out their fortune. Augusta, who had been wise with her money, lived comfortably until her death in 1895, but Horace was forced to work at menial jobs and died almost penniless. His dying words to Baby Doe in 1899 were reported to be, "Hang on to the Matchless!" (a worked out mine in Leadville). It is improbable that he really gave her this advice, as they had earlier lost this property to foreclosure, but she did return and lived in the silver mine's abandoned tool shack. In 1935 this now haggard and almost toothless old woman was found dead in her cabin, possibly succumbing to the cold.

The town of Buckskin Joe flourished for only a few years. It became the county seat of Park County and at one time boasted nearly 5,000 residents, two hotels and 14 businesses including a southern-leaning newspaper, *"The Western Pioneer."* By the mid 1870's, the free gold was gone and the town was deserted. In the 1950's, what was left of the town was moved by truck nearly 80 miles away to become a tourist attraction near the Royal Gorge Bridge. The buildings were restored to look like an old gold mining town, including a reproduction of the Tabor Store and a dance hall. In 2012 the restored town was again moved to Gunnison County to be a private museum for billionaire Bill Koch. What remains today at the site of this once prosperous little city are only square outlines of rocks where shacks once stood and thousands of discarded tin cans and bottles from thousands of untidy prospectors.

Nearby is the cemetery which is still used today by the town of Alma. It is widely reported that a veiled apparition of Miss Silverheels can be seen on moonless nights kneeling and weeping at various gravesites for victims of the small pox epidemic of 1861. Until the writing of this book, my only visit to Buckskin Joe was in 1982 for the burial of a friend named Mickey. He, like many others buried there, came to America to find fortune only to find an early demise due to the harsh conditions of the area. (His end came from a driving error in snow.) In August, 2010 I visited Buckskin Cemetery with my friend, Erik Swanson, to drink a toast in honor of his parents buried there and to visit graves of departed friends, including a real Jake Lewis whose headstone reads, "The miner who never gave up." Erik has lived almost his entire life in the town of Alma and is a direct descendant of those hardy miners who came to the area during the Colorado Gold Rush. Erik was very valuable in providing accurate local history for this story, and I thank him. He pointed out to me that you cannot see Mount Silverheels from anywhere in Buckskin Canyon, that there is no written record of a small pox epidemic, and there are no grave markers surviving from 1861 as they were crudely made of wood. The legend of Silverheels may be no more than just a good story, but I believe it to be true.

The site of Buckskin Joe is only two miles uphill from the town of Alma, Colorado, and lies a few miles below Kite Lake, the Bristlecone pines of Windy Ridge, and Mount Lincoln, which at the time of the story was thought to be the tallest peak in America. Few visit the town site, or can even find it for that matter, as so little remains of the once bustling little city. Most boom towns couldn't live on once the free gold was gone; but a few, such as nearby Alma, Fairplay, and Breckenridge did continue to thrive. Had the town survived, at 10,761 feet in elevation, Buckskin Joe would be the highest town in America.

Tom Knebel lives in Fort Collins and may be reached at:
RoadToBuckskinJoe@gmail.com

Acknowledgements

This book was written over a period of six years as a series of short assignments for Rebecca Hill's writing class in Fort Collins, Colorado. Stories were improved by suggestions from Rebecca and fellow class members. Thank you: Rebecca, Holly, Renate, Kathy, Paul S., Joanne, Marianne, Paul V., Ellie and others.

Editing, historical correcting, and suggestions were made by friends and relatives. Thank you: Holly, Dennis S., Erik, Beth, Gail, Marsha, Lon, Ron, Tom, Alan, Dennis H., Don, Linda, Mandy, Curt, Mike V. and others.

The letter from Becky was written by Brynna Kinney.

When I was a young man I enjoyed listening to tales of those a half century, more or less, older than I. All those listed below left this world years ago, but their stories remained with me to be retold in this book. Thank you:

Floyd Knebel (Indiana farmer and my grandfather),

Jake Lewis, (Fairplay, Colorado prospector),

Tip Edwards (Como, Colorado hard-rock miner),

Harold Warren (Bailey, Colorado historian),

Edna Miller (early Alma, Colorado resident and one-time burro racer),

Irvin Horn (Jefferson, Colorado miner and sawyer),

Mary Kay Snell (early Fairplay resident and consummate story teller).

Most characters are modeled after friends. Thank you, you know who you are.

Artwork by Rebecca Hill, Karen Cannon, and internet freeware.

Well done Miss Silverheels, wherever you are.

Book list

Read for inspiration, ideas or facts...

Rifles for Watie (1957). Harold Keith.

Bayou Salado: The Story of South Park (1966). Virginia McConnell Simmons.

Down the Santa Fe Trail and into Mexico; the diary of Susan Shelby Magoffin, 1846-1847. Editor: Stella M. Drumm.

Outcasts of Poker Flat and other tales. (1869). Bret Harth (Francis Brett Harte).

Call of the wild; White Fang; The Sea-wolf; Short stories (1903). Jack London.

Boone's Lick: a novel (2000). Larry McMurtry.

The Battle of Glorieta: Union victory in the West (1998). Don E. Alberts.

Reflections on a Changing Family (2007). Linda Knebel Pruden.

Blood and Thunder: an Epic of American West. (2006). Hampton Sides.

Death of a Gunfighter: The Quest for Jack Slade, the West's Most Elusive Legend (2008). Dan Rottenberg.

Aunt Clara Brown: Official Pioneer (On My Own Biography) (1999). Linda Lowery.

Early mining laws of Buckskin Joe--1859 (1961). Mumey, Nolie,

Adventures of Tom Sawyer. (1876). Mark Twain (Samuel Langhorne Clemens).

Stampede to Timberline (1949). Muriel Sibell Wolle.

The Journals of Lewis and Clark, 1804-1806. Meriwether Lewis/William Clark.

Beyond the West (1871). George W. Pine.

The Road to Buckskin Joe
ED SNELL MEMORIAL FUND

This book is being sold, in part, as a means to generate support for the Ed Snell Memorial Fund. This non-profit charity provides help to improve the quality of life for people in need of emergency assistance in the South Park area of Colorado where much of this story took place. While protecting the privacy of the individuals, this fund has given assistance to many whose financial circumstances are insufficient to cover a personal tragedy.

What started as a simple foot race between the author and a friend has grown into an annual 10K event which generates much of the charity's revenues. The fund was named for Edward L. Snell, an early South Park conservationist, who was active in mining, milling and metallurgy until his death in 1975. As a young man, he ran a pack train much like the one in this book.

(read more at http://almafoundation.com/edsnellrace.htm

If you enjoyed this book, please send a small contribution and perhaps a short message to:

Alma Foundation
PO Box 27
Alma, CO 80420

Made in the USA
San Bernardino, CA
14 July 2016